HEATH'S NINETIES

Also by Michael Heath

THE COMPLETE HEATH

HEATH'S NINETIES

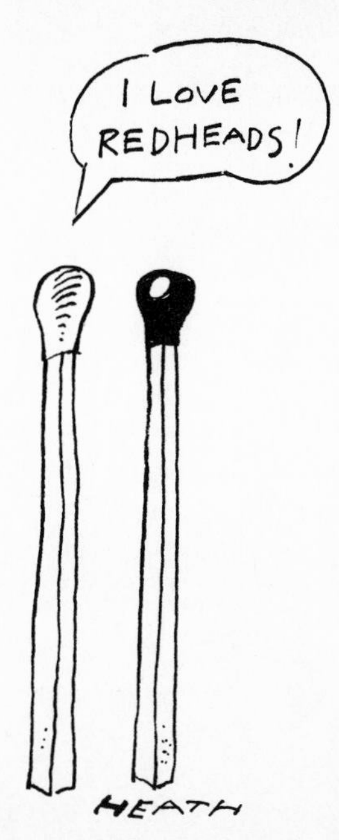

Hodder & Stoughton

First published in Great Britain in 1997
by Hodder and Stoughton
A division of Hodder Headline PLC

10 9 8 7 6 5 4 3 2 1

A Catalogue record for this title is available from
The British Library

ISBN 0 340 69531 5

Printed and bound in Great Britain

Hodder and Stoughton
A division of Hodder Headline PLC
338 Euston Road
London NW1 3BH

AD LIBS

"YOU'RE SO LATE! THIS PLACE IS NO LONGER THE PLACE TO BE SEEN IN!"
HEATH

"BANG! CRASH! MOTHERFUCK! CRUNCH! BANG! LET'S GET OUTTA HERE!"

HEATH
"HOW LONG DID THE DOCTOR SAY IT WOULD BE, BEFORE THE PROZAC KICKED IN?"

"COULDN'T YOU JUST GIVE HIM HIS REDUNDANCY, AND LEAVE IT AT THAT?"

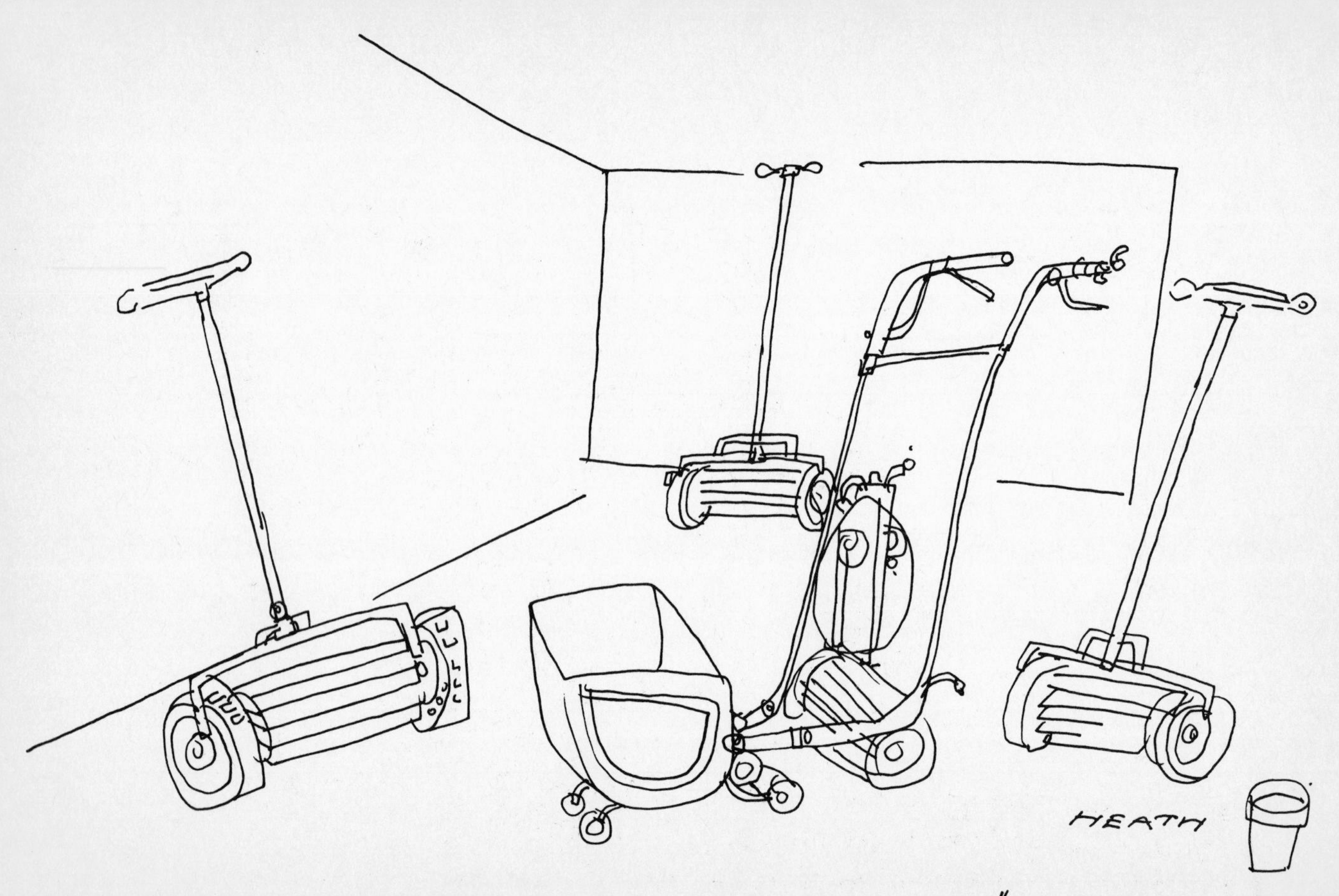

"GENTLEMEN, THERE'S A GRASS AMONGST US."

"LOOK, I'M NOT SURE I CAN SUSTAIN A LONG TERM RELATIONSHIP IF YOU DON'T LET ME SEE ANYBODY ELSE."

I FEEL SORT OF GUILTY, HE WASN'T GAY WHEN I STARTED GOING OUT WITH HIM
HEATH

MY THERAPIST HAS TAUGHT ME TO SHOP WITHOUT DROPPING
HOES
HEATH

IF I EVER HAVE A BABY, I'D HAVE IT IN HARVEY NICHOLS
HEATH

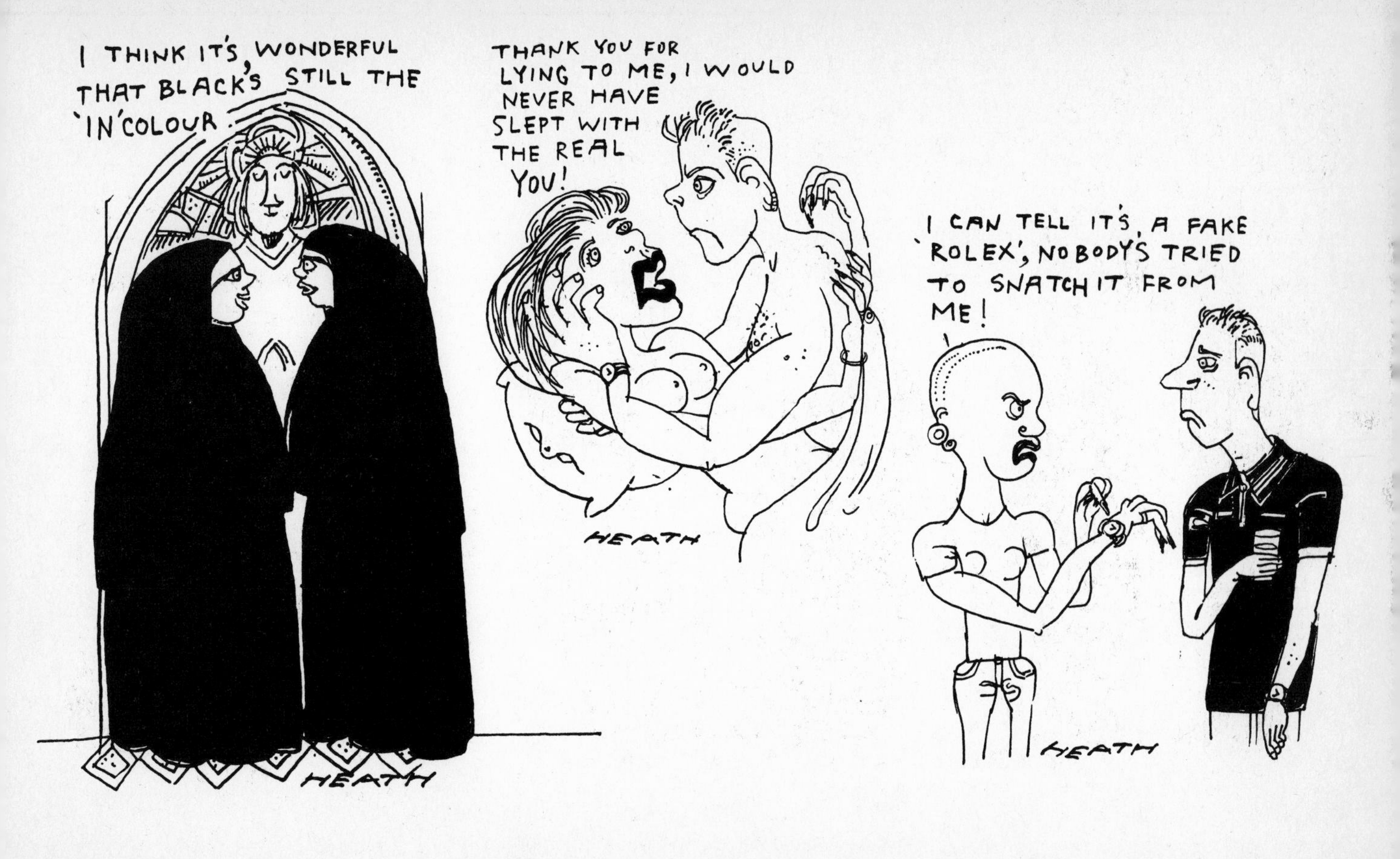
I THINK IT'S WONDERFUL THAT BLACK'S STILL THE 'IN' COLOUR.
HEATH
THANK YOU FOR LYING TO ME, I WOULD NEVER HAVE SLEPT WITH THE REAL YOU!
HEATH
I CAN TELL IT'S A FAKE 'ROLEX', NOBODY'S TRIED TO SNATCH IT FROM ME!
HEATH

MY SON'S GONE GAY!
SO!?
OH, IT'S JUST THAT I'D HOPED....
...HE'D BE LESS CONVENTIONAL!

'I'VE TAKEN AN INCH OFF THE HEM, NOW YOU MUST TELL THE SURGEON HOW YOU WOULD LIKE TO BE ALTERED.'

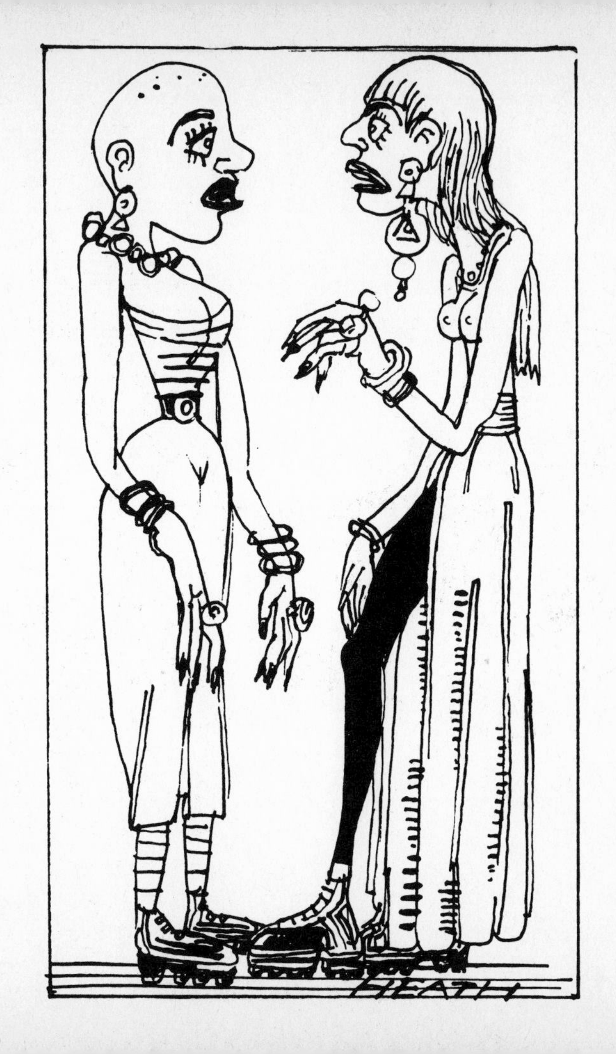

'THAT'S THE LAST TIME I GO OUT WITH A POLITICIAN. HE KEPT WANTING ME TO DO U TURNS!'

THE OUTLAW

(The *Spectator*)

THE YEAR 2000, MICHAEL COMMON IS THE LAST PERSON TO SMOKE IN ENGLAND. HE ALSO DRINKS ALCOHOL AND EATS THE WRONG FOODS. A FUGITIVE! ON THE WRONG SIDE OF THE LAW!
WHEEEEEEEEE
POLICE
WOOF
WOOF!
TO BE CONTINUED...
HEATH

MICHAEL COMMON IS THE LAST SMOKER IN THE YEAR 2000. HE IS ON THE RUN FROM THE AUTHORITIES. A FUGITIVE!
I'VE GOT AWAY, I'VE MADE IT!
COUGH! COUGH! GASP! GASP!
WE'VE BEEN PASSIVE SMOKED!
HEATH

THE YEAR 2000. MICHAEL COMMON THE LAST SMOKER IN ENGLAND, RESTS IN HIS HIDEAWAY FROM THE POLICE, LISTENING TO HIS FAVOURITE RECORDS
CRAVENA
FULL OF FLAVOUR
SMOKE GETS IN YOUR EYES
HEATH

THE YEAR 2000. THE POLICE ARE STILL PURSUING MICHAEL COMMON THE LAST SMOKER IN ENGLAND. AT LAST THEY THINK THEY HAVE A LEAD....
TONIGHT PIT BULL FIGHTING
I'VE GOT A TRAIL SIR! CIGARETTE ENDS!
COUGH!
COUGH!
HEATH

2000 AD. MICHAEL COMMON THE LAST SMOKER IN ENGLAND ENJOYS A CIGARETTE BEFORE TURNING IN
MEANWHILE, A HUNDRED MILES AWAY, A SNIFFER DOG SLEEPS
ZZZZ
ZZZ
SUDDENLY!!
SNIFF!
SNIFF!
SNIFF!!
WILL MICHAEL COMMON BE CAUGHT? HAS HE A CHANCE?
POLICE
POLICE

THE YEAR 2000. MICHAEL COMMON IS THE LAST SMOKER IN ENGLAND, HOUNDED BY THE POLICE, AND NOW OUT OF CIGARETTES AND FRANTIC!!
MUESLI RESTAURANT
OO WHEEEEEEEE
WOOF! WOOF!
DE! DA! DE! DA
WHEEEEEEE
WOOF! WOOF!
YOU MUST HAVE MORE MUESLI!
I FEEL SO MUCH FITTER!
YES- WE FEEL MUCH FITTER DON'T WE?
NO SMOKING BY PAIN OF DEATH!
HE DIVES INTO A MEAN ALLEY SUDDENLY HE SPIES A DISCARDED CIGARETTE END!
HE REALISES HE IS NOT ALONE!
HIS HEART BEGINS TO POUND
THUD THUD
IF YOUR PARENTS SMOKE OR DRINK TURN THEM IN TO US THE HEALTH POLICE
HEATH

THE YEAR 2000 MICHAEL COMMON SPYS A TRIM ANKLE AND CIGARETTE END! MAYBE HE IS NOT THE LAST SMOKER IN ENGLAND! HE SETS OFF AT A PACE IN PURSUIT OF HIS DESIRE....
PASSIVE SMOKING CARRIES THE DEATH PENALTY
GROSS
THE SATURATED FAT BOYS RULE! OK?
MUESLI ST FORMERLY TOBACCO LANE
REPORT YOUR WEIGHT TO THE HEALTH POLICE!
ALL ALCOHOL KILLS
BEWARE SUGAR !!!
SALT
CLICK! CLICK!
CHOLESTEROL ALLEY
CLICK!
HEATH
SHE WAS ALL HE HAD EVER DARED DREAM OF ...
GOT A LIGHT LUV? COUGH! COUGH!
JUST LIKE MUMMY!
...HER BREATH SMELT OF GIN AND CIGARETTES! SHE WORE A REAL FUR COAT....

THE YEAR 2000. MICHAEL COMMON THINKS HE IS THE LAST SMOKER IN ENGLAND. BUT HE MEETS QUEENIE A SOULMATE SHE INVITES HIM BACK TO HER FLAT FOR A SNACK.....
GOD! THOSE FAT SATURATED CHIPS AND BEEF BURGERS WERE GREAT!
PARDON ME!
I HOPE YOU STILL HAVE ROOM FOR SUET AND TREACLE PUD?
WHITE SLICED LOAF
MORE CREME-DE-MENTHE?
NOT YET I'VE STILL GOT HALF A GLASS LEFT
POP!
AFTER THREE OR FOUR WALNUT WHIPS, MICHAEL STARTS TO REMINISCE...
WHAT HAPPENED TO THE GOOD OLD DAYS WHEN WE COULD EAT LIKE THAT EVERY NIGHT?
AND WHAT HAPPENED TO ALL OUR OLD FRIENDS?
THEY ALL DIED MY DEAR
OR DID THEY?

THE YEAR 2000 MICHAEL COMMON THOUGHT HE WAS THE ONLY SMOKER IN ENGLAND. HOWEVER HE HAS FOUND A FRIEND IN QUEENIE. AFTER A HEAVY SATURATED FAT MEAL, MICHAEL REMEMBERS OLD FRIENDS!
PETER, WHO DRANK 18 UNITS A WEEK! HE MUST BE DEAD. NO BODY COULD TAKE SUCH PUNISMENT!
JENNY, SHE WAS NEARLY 13 STONE! AND REFUSED TO DIET! SURELY SHE MUST HAVE GONE
SIDNEY. WHO REFUSED TO EAT FIBRE!! AND MADE ESPRESSO IN HIS BASEMENT TO DRINK!!
HE SOUNDS LIKE MY KIND OF MAN
I'D LOVE YOU TO HAVE MET SIDNEY HE DIDN'T CARE ABOUT ANYTHING! HE'D EAT ADDITIVES.. ARTIFICIAL COLOURING.. HE HAD GUTS!
KNOCK! KNOCK! KNOCK!
IT'S THE SMOKE POLICE!
SUDDENLY THERE'S A LOUD KNOCK ON THE DOOR!!

THE YEAR 2000 · MICHAEL COMMON AND HIS NEW FRIEND QUEENIE ARE ENJOYING A BANNED MEAL OF POT NOODLES AND DONUTS.
KNOCK! KNOCK!
PLEASE LET ME IN!!
IT'S ME PETER!
18 UNITS A WEEK PETER! HE'S ALIVE!
I WAS CAUGHT BY THE HEALTH POLICE! I WAS PUT ON A FITNESS COURSE... A FAT FREE DIET....
CAFFEINE FREE COFFEE! NON ALCOHOLIC WINE!
GULP!
THEY LET HIM IN → HE LOOKED 20 YEARS OLDER!
I JOG EVERY DAY....
I DON'T SMOKE
I NEVER TAKE SUGAR OR SALT!
I SLEEP 8 HOURS A NIGHT
I HAVE NOT HAD A DRINK FOR MONTHS
I FEEL REALLY GREAT!
OH, PLEASE YOU MUST HELP ME!
I'VE BECOME SO SMUG!
MORE TO COME....

THE YEAR 2000 MICHAEL COMMON IS STILL ON THE RUN FROM THE HEALTH POLICE...
I'LL DIVE IN HERE!
EXIT
EXIT
FILM ARCHIVE
FIBRE PLUS
EXIT
POLYUNSATURATES NEWS ON THE MARCH
FLICKER
FLICKER
EARLY EUTHANASIA FOOTAGE
NEWS ON THE MARCH
FLICKER
FLICKER
CIGARETTE MY LOVE?
S.S. HAPPY
STAY TUNED....

MICHAEL COMMON IS LONELY. DEPRESSED. SOBER.
IT IS THE YEAR 2000 AND HE IS IN HIDING.
I NEED THE WARMTH OF FEMALE COMPANY, I WANT TO BE WITH QUEENIE!
SMOKE GETS IN YOUR EYES CLICK! SMOKE GETS IN YOUR EYE
2000 UNFILTERED CIGARETTES
BUTTERED ROLL KILLS MAN
HEATH
HI! MIKE
COUGH! COUGH!
HOW WAS HE TO FIND HER AGAIN?......
OK HOLD HIM!......
BUT WHAT IF HE WERE CAUGHT?
NOOO
NOW! PUT THE SEAT BELT ON HIM!
PLEASE!
TAKE IT OFF!
AND THEN THE INTERROGATION!
IT'S FOR YOUR OWN GOOD
EVERYBODY ELSE WEARS ONE....
WHAT IF EVERYBODY BEHAVED LIKE YOU?
NOTHING COULD BE WORSE THAN ROOM 101!
DO NOT LAUGH
SALT KILLS
QUEENIE!
LOVE IS BAD FOR YOUR HEART
DON'T LOVE
ARE YOU OVERWEIGHT?
HE HAD TO FIND QUEENIE!

THE YEAR 2000: MICHAEL COMMON IS SEARCHING FOR HIS LONG LOST FRIEND QUEENIE. SHE SMOKES, SO DOES HE. IT IS AGAINST THE LAW!
SHUTUP!
CALL THE POLICE HE'S NOT WATCHING T.V.!
YOO! HOO! UP HERE MICHAEL
OH QUEENIE YOO! HOO!
MORE THAN ONE UNIT OF ALCOHOL A YEAR KILLS!
DIETARY FIBRE DOES SOMETHING TO A MAN
I LIKE A MAN WITH FIBRE!
MICHAEL MAKES HIS WAY TOWARDS FAMILIAR SOUNDS
HERE MICHAEL! HERE.
COUGH! COUGH!
I'M COMING! I'M COMING!
QUEENIE!
MICHAEL!
HAVE YOU GOT A LIGHT?
NO, I THOUGHT YOU'D HAVE ONE!
AFTER THE JOYOUS REUNION
YOU MEAN YOU HAVEN'T GOT A LIGHT!
NO!
THE TENSION RISES!
LOOK, I'M NOT GOING TO RISK ARREST BY GOING OUT TO GET A LIGHT!!
WELL, YOU'RE GOING TO HAVE TO! I'M NOT GOING! YOU MAKE ME SICK!
SILLY COW!
WILL THINGS WORK OUT?....

IN A FITFUL SLEEP MICHAEL COMMON DREAMS OF HIS DEAD PARENTS
CHASER
SCOTCH
HIS FATHER WAS ONE HELL OF A CHARACTER ! HE DRANK AT LUNCH TIMES!!
HIS MOTHER LIVED IN THE KITCHEN AND SMOKED 20 CIGARETTES A DAY!! WITH NO FILTERS!
HEATH
WHAT WAS IT ABOUT HIS PARENTS ?....?..
I KNOW!
I'VE GOT IT!!
THEY WERE HAPPY!
AND SEVERAL POUNDS OVER WEIGHT!

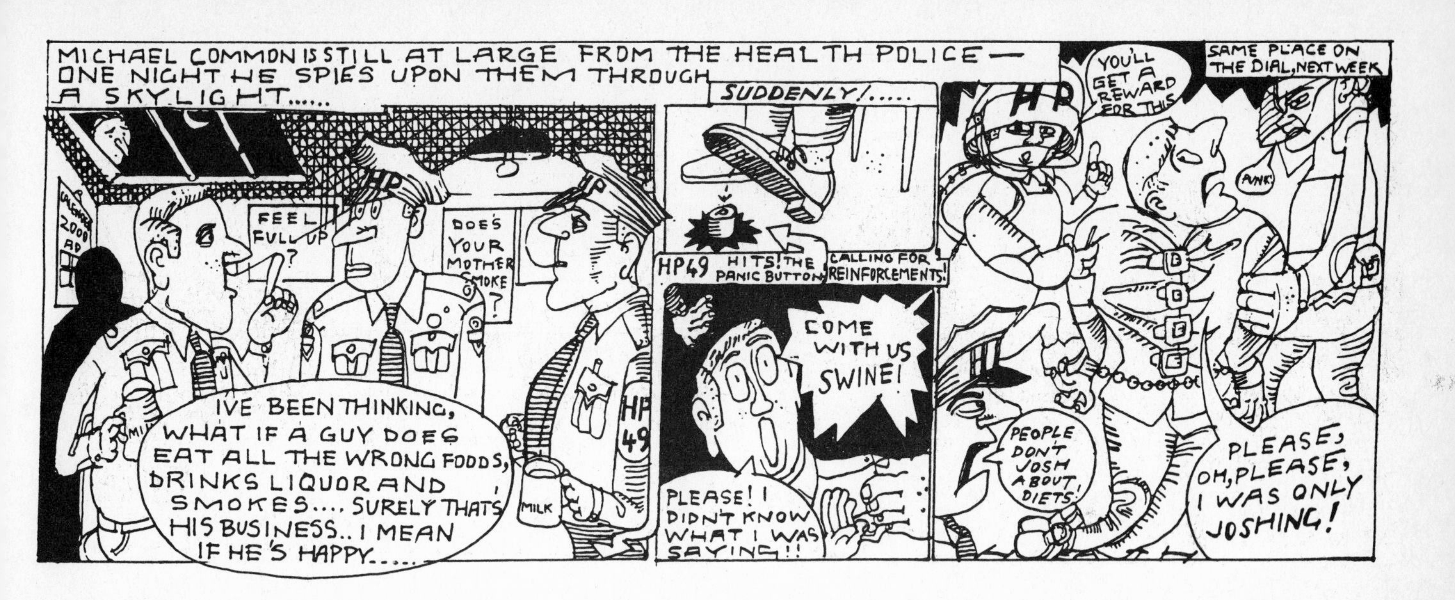
MICHAEL COMMON IS STILL AT LARGE FROM THE HEALTH POLICE — ONE NIGHT HE SPIES UPON THEM THROUGH A SKYLIGHT......
CALENDAR 2008 AD
FEEL FULL UP ?
DOES YOUR MOTHER SMOKE ?
IVE BEEN THINKING, WHAT IF A GUY DOES EAT ALL THE WRONG FOODS, DRINKS LIQUOR AND SMOKES.... SURELY THATS HIS BUSINESS.. I MEAN IF HE'S HAPPY.....
MILK
HP 49
SUDDENLY!.....
HP49 HITS! THE PANIC BUTTON
CALLING FOR REINFORCEMENTS!
COME WITH US SWINE!
PLEASE! I DIDN'T KNOW WHAT I WAS SAYING!!
YOU'LL GET A REWARD FOR THIS
PEOPLE DON'T JOSH ABOUT DIETS!
SAME PLACE ON THE DIAL, NEXT WEEK
PLEASE, OH, PLEASE, I WAS ONLY JOSHING!

GREAT BORES OF TODAY

(*Private Eye*)
with words thanks to
Ian Hislop, Barry Fantoni,
Richard Ingrams and
Nick Newman

'... This is a British Telecom announcement the number you have called has not been recognised the code for Presleydale has been changed for three figure numbers redial using the prefix 0149623 for four figure numbers insert the digits 827 after the 4. For example if you are dialling Presleydale 373 you should now dial 0148279623 and then the number if however the Presleydale subscriber has taken the number after June 6th the number it now falls under Wisleydale if your phone has a squash function press squash followed by 779 for the new Wisleydale codes British Telecom has not charged you for this call. This is a British Telecom announcement the number you have called has not been ...'

'... there's nothing in them there's never anything to read and look at these clothes who on earth do they think is going to wear them? and is this an advertisement or is it an article? you can't tell look at this a whole supplement on lipstick who cares? this month's is worse than ever and who are all these people? I've never heard of any of them she just looks ridiculous in those boots there's nothing to read and they cost a fortune this one is nearly three quid and there's six pages of photos of paella really what is that about? op-art handbags? no one is interested in that oh no not another Kate Moss photo spread it's always the same old crowd and they're all so skinny nobody wants to see that there's absolutely nothing to read what star sign are you? Libra isn't it? oh that's good romance is in the air for you and I've got a new job after you with that one ...'

'... if ever there was a fix this was it did you see it? I was round at my brother-in-law's he's got Sky I was just opening a can of lager in the kitchen and when I went back in it was all over he was lying on the floor and Bruno was walking around telling everyone he was going to be the new world champion it's got to be a joke hasn't it? it's the same old story he's never had a fight with anyone worth talking about except Tyson and he murdered him you see the way it works is you need to get a couple of preliminaries under your belt in this case it's the WBA or it might be the IBM or even the BMW and then you a get a crack at the world title but in Bruno's case they just get stiffs for him to knock down we've seen it all before just take Eubank he's typical and the Asian boy what's he called? Prince someone? course when Frank gets up against real opposition they'll knock his head off he should stick to panto we saw him in *Aladdin* at Richmond and he was brilliant he kept saying "oh yes he is Harry" my sister's little boy Kevin loves him and at least he's English no he's good entertainment so what if it's fixes? who cares ...?'

'. . . who on earth is this man Paul Bambergascoigne? is that it? some disc jockey from Radio 2? if we wanted a silly American with all his rock and pop then we would tune in to Terry Wogan I mean what is this classical collection thing? Why don't we just call it Top of the Pops and be done with it? in at Number One? what's that supposed to mean? what's wrong with Composer of the Week I'd like to know ... Beethoven Brahms sometimes a new johnny you hadn't heard of but you didn't mind that why doesn't he just stop talking and let us listen to the music? *the beautiful haunting refrain of Wagner's Parsifal echoing through the mists of time and bubbling under...* lord luvaduck I've never heard such rubbish in all my life switch over to Classic FM darling for heaven's sake and let's have Henry Kelly now there's a chap who really knows about classical music. . .'

'... you won't be able to buy a pint soon not if the EC has its way it'll be 2.8 litres and you'll have to pay ecus for it and that'll just be the start of it do you know you can't buy 6 eggs in France you have to buy 5 because the men from Brussels have said so it's lunacy isn't it? it's the officials going mad did you see that story about the farmer in Devon who wasn't allowed to make cider because his apples were the wrong shape? he went broke and shot himself and what about the British sausage? apparently it has to be between 18 and 19 centimetres long or it's reclassified as a fruit no seriously you don't believe me but it's true a carrot is now officially a dairy product I read it in the *Daily Mail* or was it the *Sunday Telegraph*? anyway English mustard is going to be a thing of the past it has to be Moutarde Regulière just like gravy that's going to be designated as jam from now on now I'm a thirty-six waist and my wife went to buy me a pair of trousers could she find them? could she? all she could get was something called M16 L-R what's that all about? it's lunacy it's those men in Brussels going mad we're on a hand-cart to hell and I gather they're going to paint all the postboxes yellow ...'

'... I mean basically it's just Gallic temperament he's passionate he's moody he's like Gerard Depardieu in that film same sort of bloke same nose he's like Jean-Paul Sartre in a football shirt you know it's no wonder he lost his rag you only have to go to a match to see the abuse that a player like Eric is subjected to the things they yell at him I'm only surprised he's never done it before but hats off to him it's about time I wouldn't fine him no way I'd give him three grand to kick some of those morons I mean Eric's a genius he writes poetry he paints he cooks he speaks French and when it comes to football his boots are garlic-flavoured his feet literally do the talking which is why he kicked that bloke in the head the press have turned him into a monster but he's not like that at all he's a cultured bloke he's a renaissance man I mean Albert Camus for example was a goalkeeper and was it Voltaire who played in midfield ...'

'... it's disgusting apparently it's got every depravity known to man in one play rape masturbation micturition and frottage apparently and people are walking out in droves particularly after this woman sucks this man's eyes out and then rapes him or is it the other way around? I mean the Royal Court is well known for its controversial drama but this is the worst ever apparently there's metrication and frontage and stimulatio people have fainted and had to be carried out the writer is only 23 you wonder where she learnt all this stuff imbroglio and desiderata which apparently they do after the soldier comes back and they put him in the floorboards and then they tremulate all over him it's all there it's absolutely disgusting what they get away with and the really sick thing is that people pay to see it amazing Julian and I are going on Thursday ...'

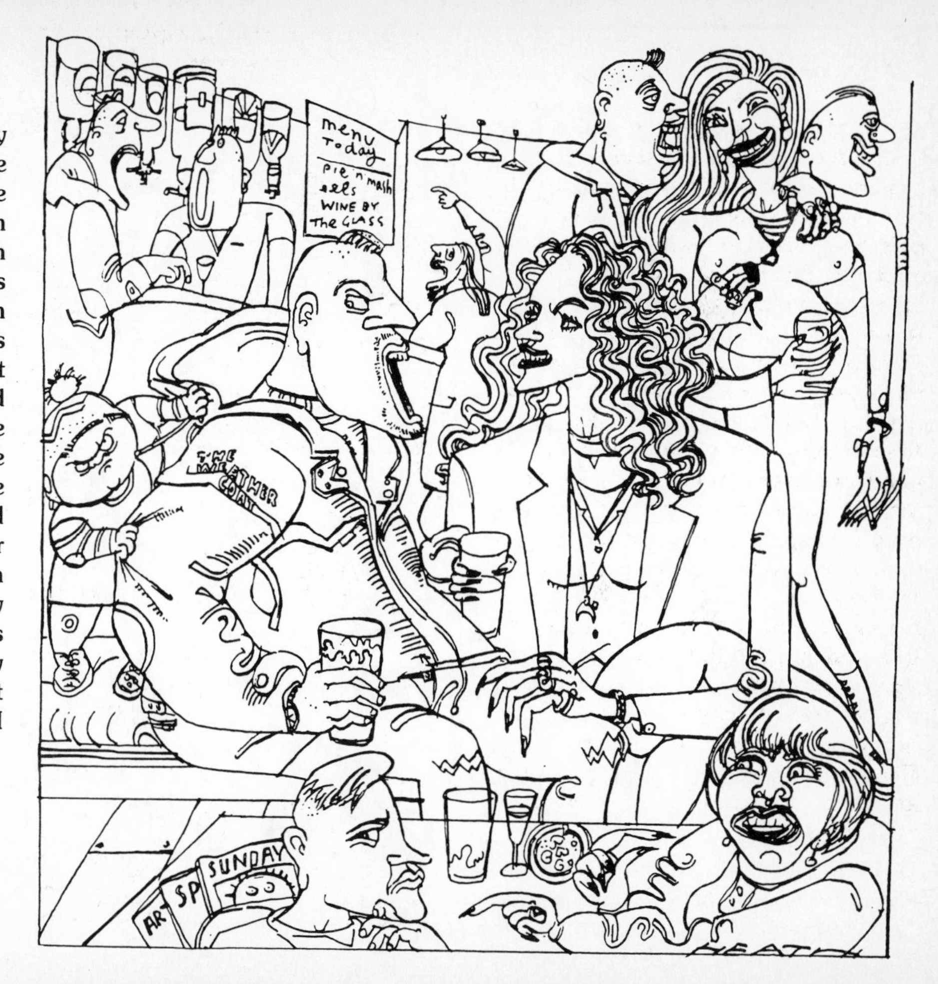

‘... there was absolutely nothing on to watch ... bugger all ... I’ve never known a Christmas like it ... four channels and every one a bummer ... we hardly turned the set on apart from obviously One Foot in the Grave which was brilliant and The Thin Blue Line that was good but apart from that there was nothing else oh Wallace and Gromit was great and I really enjoyed Hook which I hadn’t seen before but the standard was pitiful and there was nothing religious except Alan Bennett but then he’s always good it was pathetic you’d think they’d make some effort to put on *something* worth watching where were all the great films? admittedly it was good to see E.T. again, and Indiana Jones is pretty amazing and My Fair Lady was good fun as always and Rear Window is a classic I can watch that again and again did you see The Coronation Street Special? that was *really* moving but generally when you look back there was literally nothing on at all except Those Magnificent Men In Their Flying Machines which was the one programme the whole family wanted to watch it had Terry Thomas Peter Cook Dudley Moore Hancock no really it was a pity it clashed with Christmas With Richard and Judy... but there was absolutely nothing on ...’

'... it's brilliant all you need to do is configure your modem to autodial your service provider and then you're online to a global network which enables you to browse the worldwide web surf the news-groups ftp to a site to grab an update for your display driver or anything you want now I've got an email address anyone can reach me instantly all you need is a PC with a fast serial port a V32 modem minimum or ISDN if you can afford it a good network connection to the PSTN and away you go it's as simple as that at 2am I was able to send the message "hello I'm on the Internet" to Colin next door only it got bounced because he hasn't got his system installed yet so I had to ring him instead but anyway it's brilliant ...'

'... 100 million quid to subsidise the opera it's outrageous do you go to the opera? no nor do I nor does anyone why should we give our money to allow a few toffs to get in to see it on the cheap? why doesn't the money go to something worthwhile? they reckon for that amount you could buy 150 kidney machines or 250 heart scanners or goodness knows how many operations for sick kiddies it's obscene when you think about it and someone on television said cancer research is crying out for money if I'd have known when I was buying my tickets that my money was all going to allow the snobs in Covent Garden to have another gin and tonic in the interval I wouldn't have bought them well I probably would actually but if I won all the money I'd give a lot of it away to a proper charity why does opera need £100 million anyway? I thought the Arts Council already gave them a fortune it's a rip-off someone should do something about it I think this week I'll try a different formula I noticed in the last three weeks there have been a lot of numbers under ten still it's only a bit of fun and what's £50 a week anyway? ...'

PARTNERS

(The *Independent*)

FAIRY STORIES HANDED DOWN FROM PARENTS TO CHILDREN OVER THE CENTURIES...
BABY BABY BUNTING, DADDY'S GONE A HUNTING, TO FETCH HIS.....ER...ER... BABY BABY BUNTING, DADDY'S GONE A HUNTING TO....ER...ER....
NO..HANG ON... TO FETCH....
MARY HAD A LITTLE LAMB WHOSE FLEECE WAS WHITE AS SNOW..... AND EVERYWHERE THAT MARY WENT THE LAMB WAS SURE TO GO.....IT.. THAT'S IT...IT FOLLOWED HER TO SCHOOL ONE DAY...DA..DE... DAMN! IT FOLLOWED HER TO SCHOOL ONE DAY........ JACK SPRATT COULD EAT NO FAT HIS WIFE COULD EAT NO LEAN....ER... BLAST!
HICKERY DICKERY DOCK THE MOUSE RAN....
NURSERY RHYMES
HEATH

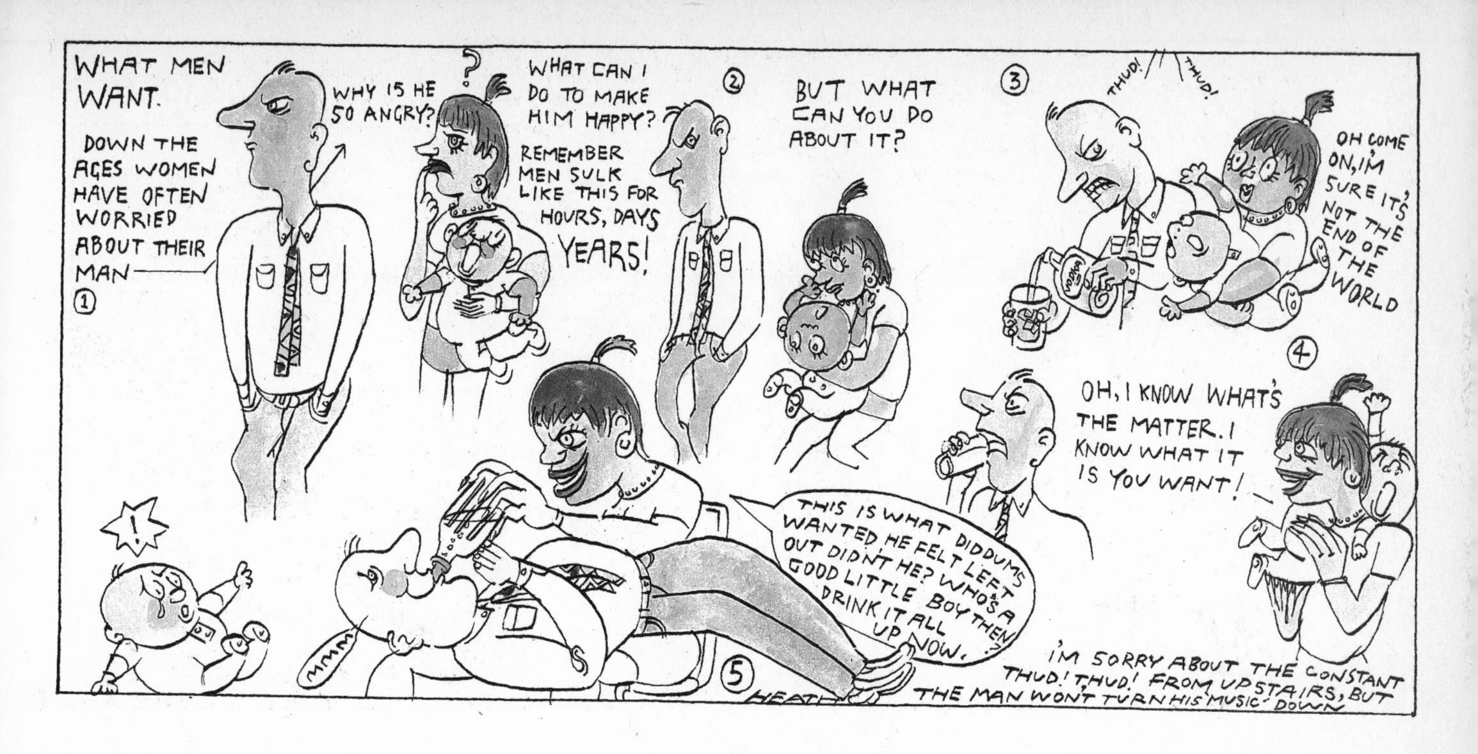
WHAT MEN WANT.
DOWN THE AGES WOMEN HAVE OFTEN WORRIED ABOUT THEIR MAN
1
WHY IS HE SO ANGRY?
?
WHAT CAN I DO TO MAKE HIM HAPPY?
REMEMBER MEN SULK LIKE THIS FOR HOURS, DAYS YEARS!
2
BUT WHAT CAN YOU DO ABOUT IT?
3
THUD!
THUD!
VODKA
OH COME ON, I'M SURE IT'S NOT THE END OF THE WORLD
4
OH, I KNOW WHAT'S THE MATTER. I KNOW WHAT IT IS YOU WANT!
!
THIS IS WHAT DIDDUMS WANTED HE FELT LEFT OUT DIDN'T HE? WHO'S A GOOD LITTLE BOY THEN? DRINK IT ALL UP NOW.
MMM
5
I'M SORRY ABOUT THE CONSTANT THUD! THUD! FROM UPSTAIRS, BUT THE MAN WON'T TURN HIS MUSIC DOWN
HEATH

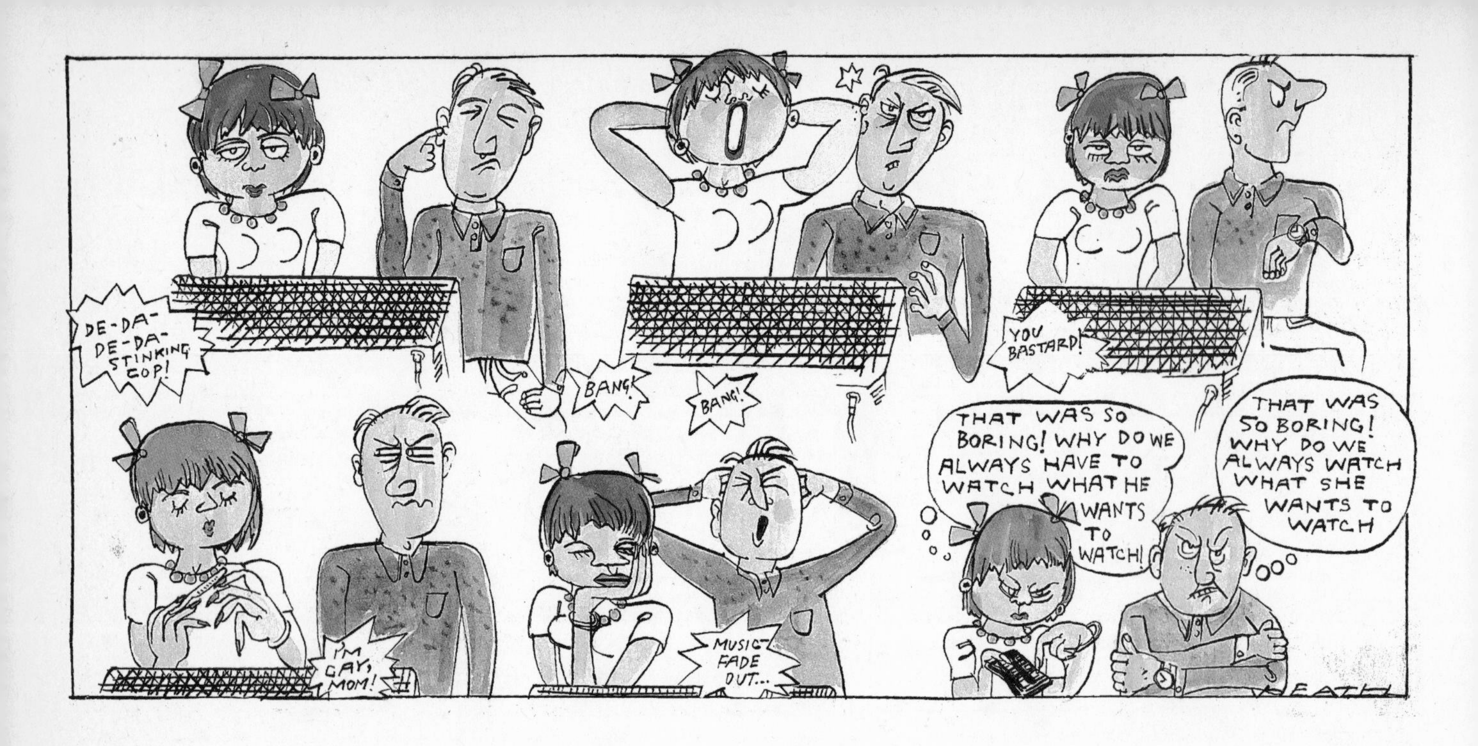
DE-DA-DE-DA-STINKING COP!
BANG!
BANG!
YOU BASTARD!
I'M GAY, MOM!
MUSIC FADE OUT...
THAT WAS SO BORING! WHY DO WE ALWAYS HAVE TO WATCH WHAT HE WANTS TO WATCH!
THAT WAS SO BORING! WHY DO WE ALWAYS WATCH WHAT SHE WANTS TO WATCH
HEATH

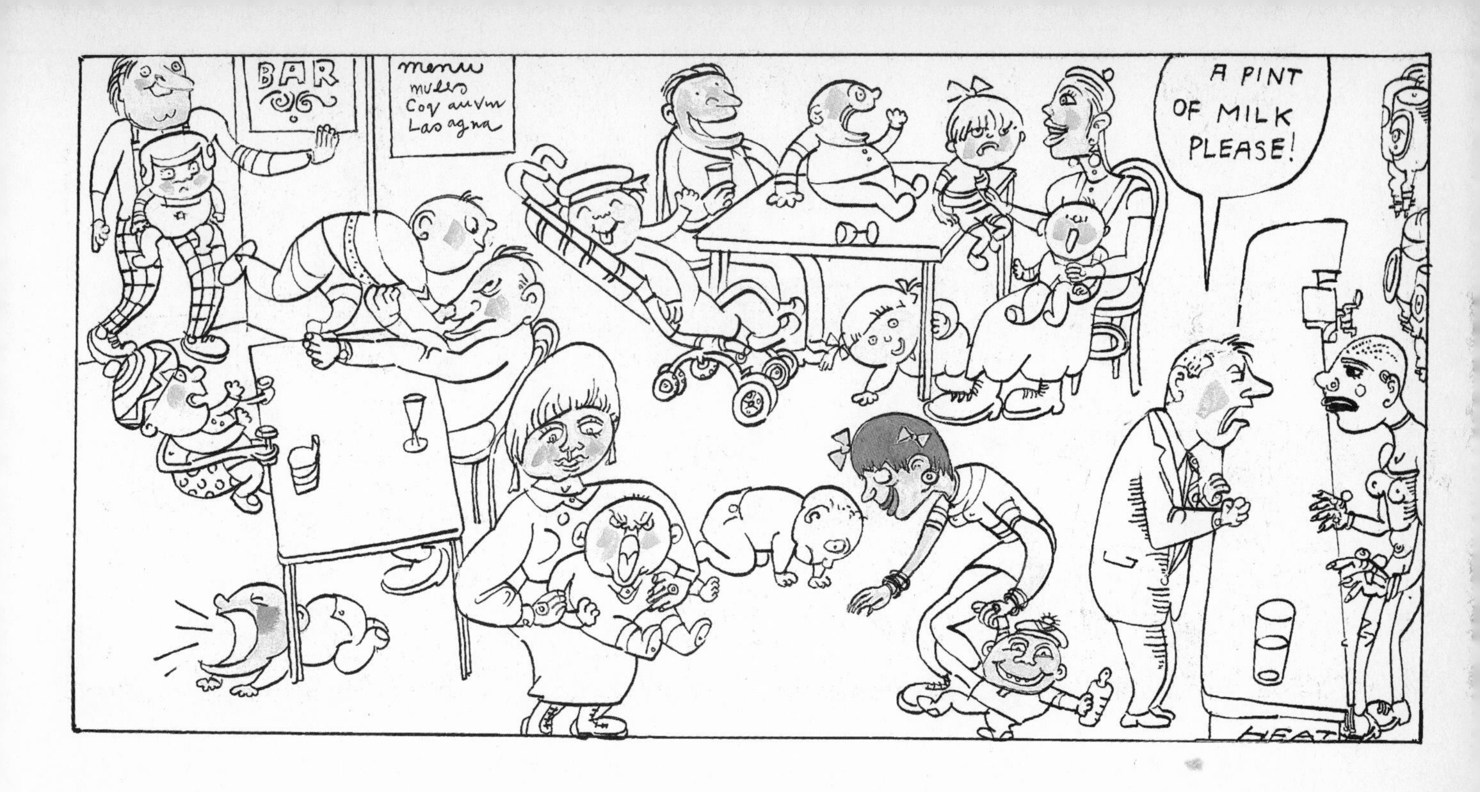
BAR
menu
mules
Coq au vin
Lasagna
A PINT OF MILK PLEASE!
HEATH

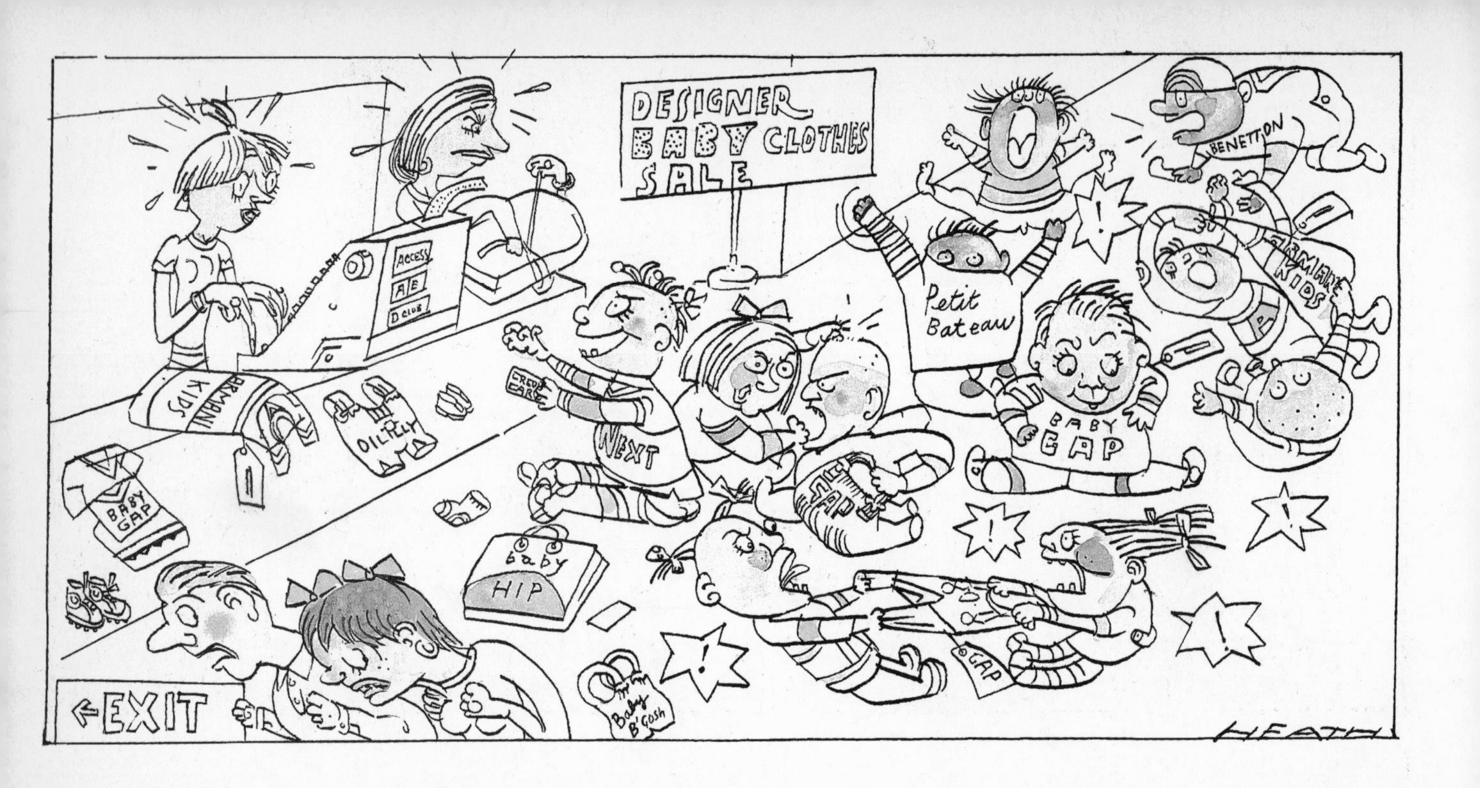
DESIGNER BABY CLOTHES SALE
ACCESS
AE
D CLUB
ARMANI KIDS
OILILY
BABY GAP
CREDIT CARD
NEXT
Petit Bateau
BENETTON
ARMANI KIDS
BABY GAP
baby HIP
GAP
Baby B'Gosh
←EXIT
HEATH

WHINE! WHINE!
GRIZZLE! GRIZZLE!
MOAN! MOAN!
7/30 AM
WHINE! WHINE!
GRIZZLE! GRIZZLE!
8/15 AM
SCREAM! COUGH! COUGH!
5 pm
WHINE! SNIFFLE!
7/30 pm
MOAN! SNIFFLE! WHINE
TIME FOR BED!
YOU'RE OVERTIRED!
8 pm
NIGHTY NIGHT SLEEP TIGHT!
MOAN! SNIFFLE! WHIMPER! ZZZZZZ
8/15pm
GOD! WHAT A DAY!
8/30pm
GRIZZLE! GRIZZLE! MOAN! MOAN! WHINE! WHINE! WHIMPER! MOAN! MOAN!
9/15pm
HEATH

IT SEEMS TO ME THAT SOME PEOPLE CAN TAKE OTHER PEOPLE FOR GRANTED....
.PEOPLE SHOULD PRAISE EACH OTHER FOR DOING....
...THE DREARY THINGS.... THE WASHING UP, THE
PICKING UP OF ENDLESS TOYS.... ..THE COOKING.. BED MAKING...
IT'S ALL PRETTY BORING, BUT HAS TO BE DONE....
...THE DAILY GRIND... SHOPPING IN THE SUPER-MARKET.... WHERE ARE YOU GOING?
TO THE PUB!
HEATH

EVER GET THAT FEELING OF DÉJÀ-VU?
BAR
VINS
ESPRES
FRENCH
POSTER
1929
HEATH

I DON'T UNDERSTAND, WHAT IS IT YOU'RE SAYING?
DIT!
WHAT ARE YOU TRYING TO SAY 'DIT', WHAT?
DIT! DIT! DIT! DIT!
WHAT DO YOU MEAN 'DIT'!?
'DIT' WHAT?
DIT! DIT!
DARLING! EXPLAIN YOURSELF! WHAT'S 'DIT'
DIT! DIT! DIT!
I NEVER UNDERSTAND A WORD HE SAYS!
HEATH

GOO! GOO! GOO! BLAP! BEEP! GOOO! GOO! DA! DA!
IS LITTLE DIDDUMS ALL RIGHT? COOCHY! COOCHY COO!
AREN'T THEY THE COUPLE WHO HAD THE BABY? THEY LOOK FAMILIAR
YES, BUT THEY DON'T GET OUT MUCH. I HAVEN'T SEEN THEM FOR ABOUT A YEAR
I LIKE TO BE TIED UP AND...
I DIDN'T SEE YOU AT THE MARLENE DUMAS SHOW. IT WAS JUST FABULOUS!
NO, I WAS AT THE SACHA DIEU BASH IT WAS JUST GREAT!
I SAW DURESSENCE— A GREAT BAGGY-ARSED BAND!
THE NEW PRINT OF 'REBECCA' AT THE EVERYMAN WAS A BLINDER!
HAVE YOU SEEN 'KIDS'?
HEATH

HENRY KING

(The *Spectator*)

IT'S SEEMS THAT I WILL BE LUCKY TO GET ANY EDUCATION AT ALL...
..SO I'LL NEED A JOB THAT DOESN'T REQUIRE TOO MUCH BRAIN.... AND PAYS A LOT
SO I'LL BECOME A MALE MODEL
HEATH

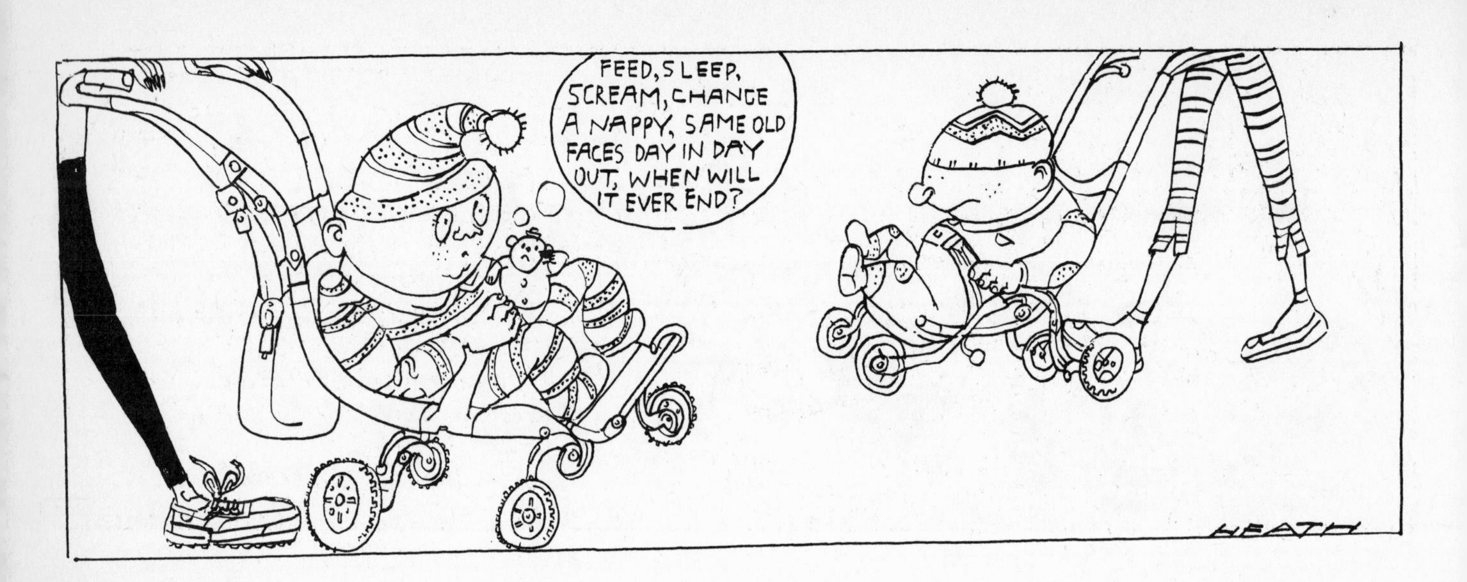
FEED, SLEEP, SCREAM, CHANGE A NAPPY, SAME OLD FACES DAY IN DAY OUT, WHEN WILL IT EVER END?
HEATH

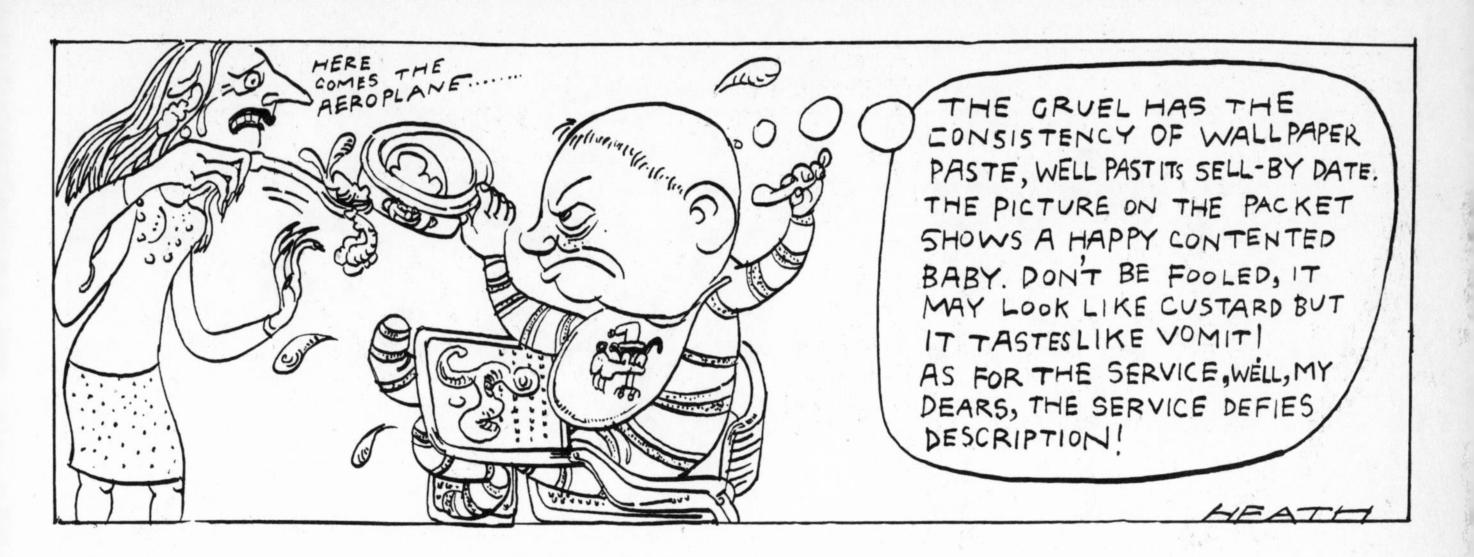
HERE COMES THE AEROPLANE........
THE GRUEL HAS THE CONSISTENCY OF WALLPAPER PASTE, WELL PAST ITS SELL-BY DATE. THE PICTURE ON THE PACKET SHOWS A HAPPY CONTENTED BABY. DON'T BE FOOLED, IT MAY LOOK LIKE CUSTARD BUT IT TASTES LIKE VOMIT! AS FOR THE SERVICE, WELL, MY DEARS, THE SERVICE DEFIES DESCRIPTION!
HEATH

I FEEL MY PRIVACY....
....IS BEING INVADED.....
....EVERY MOVE I MAKE, EVERY WHERE I GO....
......IS BEING RECORDED ON SURVEILLANCE CAMERAS!
HEATH

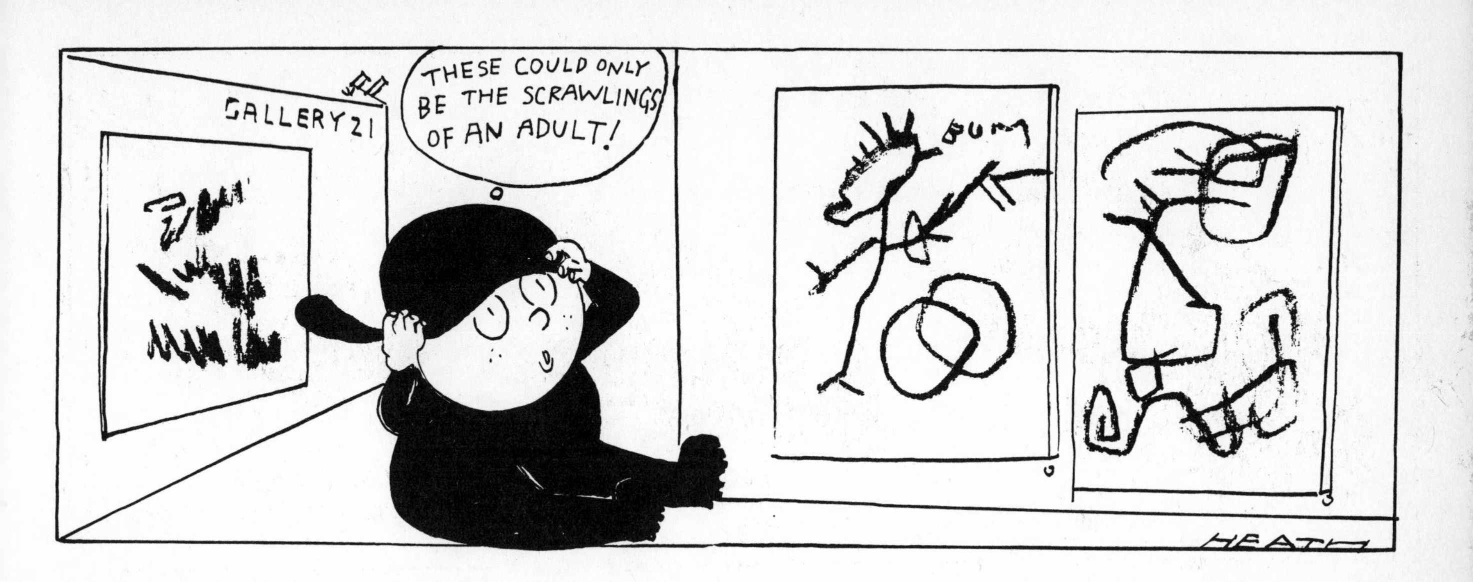
GALLERY 21
THESE COULD ONLY BE THE SCRAWLINGS OF AN ADULT!
BUM
HEATH

MOTHER CARE
NEXT
KIDS
GIEVES & HAWKES
No. 1 Savile Row, London
HEATH

HEATH

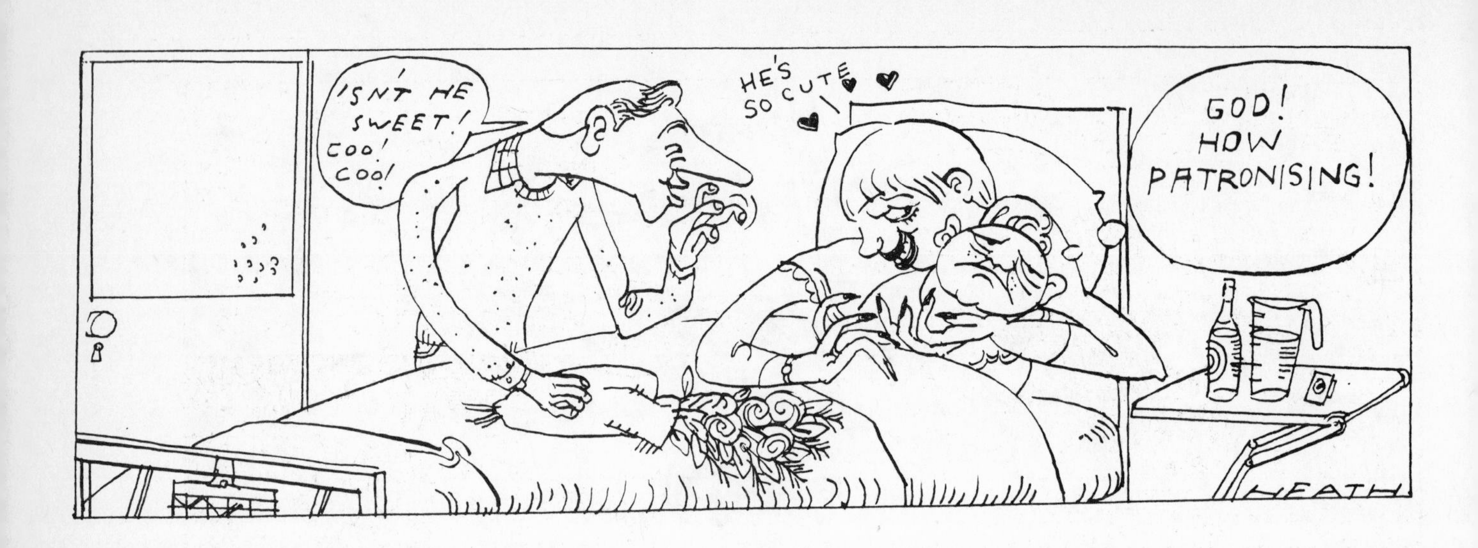
ISN'T HE SWEET! COO! COO!
HE'S SO CUTE
GOD! HOW PATRONISING!
HEATH

WADAEVADUNFURME?
LOOK! I LOVE CARTOONS! BUT I WANT YOU TO STOP! THIS CARTOON IS JUST NOT FUNNY! WHY CAN'T YOU DO SOMETHING LOVEABLE LIKE 'PEANUTS' OR FUNNY LIKE GARY LARSON? DROP THAT PEN! OR TRY TO DRAW A NICE KIND OF CUTE KID LIKE... LIKE.. YOU KNOW.
CARTOON POLICE
CARTOON POLICE
OH NO! HE'S TAKEN ON THE PERSONALITY OF THE DUMB KID HE'S BEEN DRAWING!
"IT'S LIKE DEAD OF NIGHT!"
HENRY KING

WHEN HENRY KING AWOKE ONE MORNING FROM UNEASY DREAMS HE FOUND HIMSELF TRANSFORMED IN HIS BED INTO A HUGE GOOFY YOUTH!
WADYAEVADUNFURME?
OH, MY GOD!
BAYWATCH
ROCK
MTV
THE THUDS
WICKED
SMASH HITS
HEATH

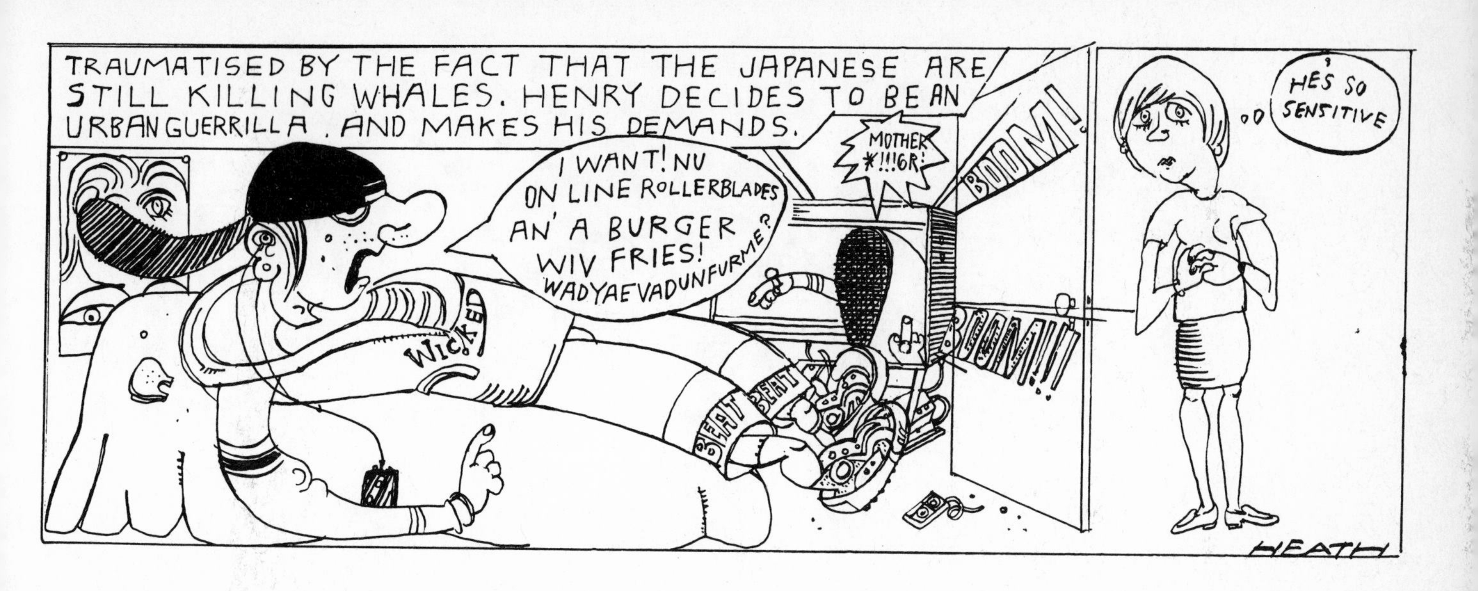
TRAUMATISED BY THE FACT THAT THE JAPANESE ARE STILL KILLING WHALES. HENRY DECIDES TO BE AN URBAN GUERRILLA, AND MAKES HIS DEMANDS.
I WANT! NU ON LINE ROLLERBLADES AN' A BURGER WIV FRIES! WADYAEVADUNFURME?
MOTHER *!!!GR!
BOOM!
BOOM!!
WICKED
BEAT BEAT BEAT
HE'S SO SENSITIVE
HEATH

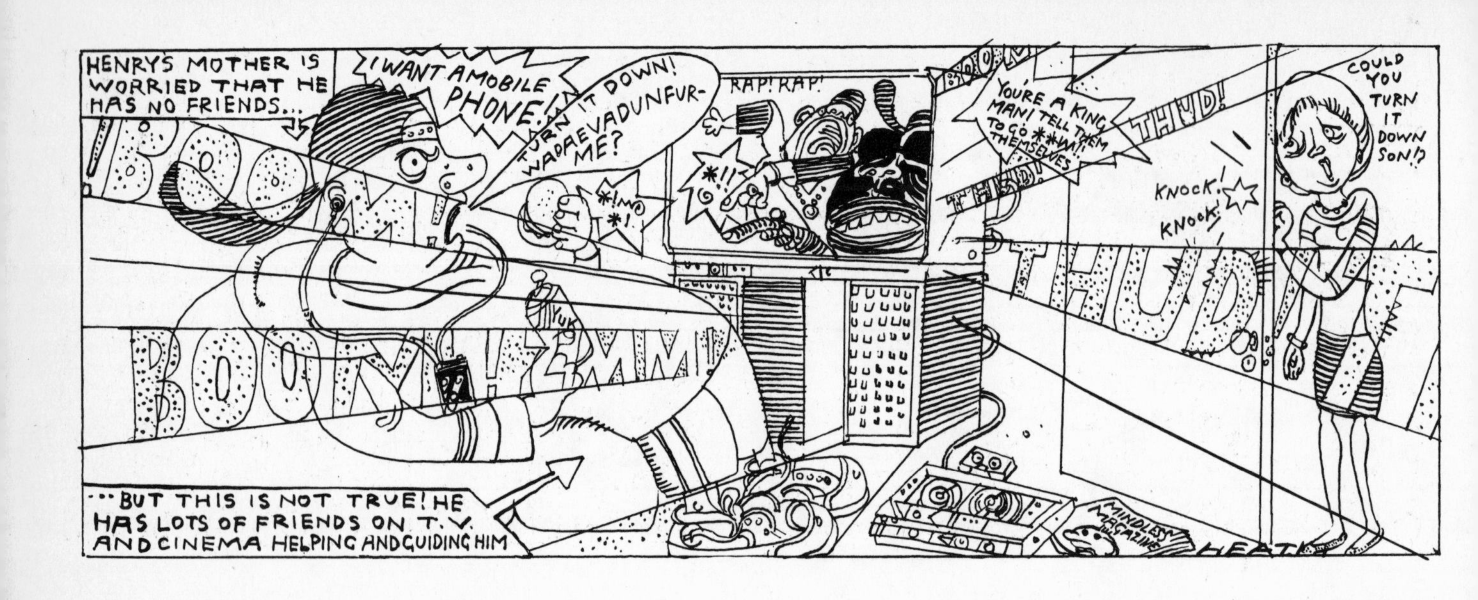

HENRYS MOTHER IS WORRIED THAT HE HAS NO FRIENDS...
I WANT A MOBILE PHONE!
TURN IT DOWN! WADAEVADUNFUR-ME?
RAP! RAP!
YOU'RE A KING MAN! TELL THEM TO GO **!! THEMSELVES
COULD YOU TURN IT DOWN SON!?
KNOCK! KNOCK!
THUD!
THUD!
BOOM!
BOOM!
YUK
...BUT THIS IS NOT TRUE! HE HAS LOTS OF FRIENDS ON T.V. AND CINEMA HELPING AND GUIDING HIM
MINDLESS MAGAZINE
HEATH

THANK YOU FOR BEARING WITH ME, READER, BUT I THINK HENRY MAY BE TRYING TO GET OFF HIS BED!!!!
UUFF! ERR! UUUFF!
ARRR! VURR! GASP! WADAEVADUNFURME!
EEEEERRR!
BOOM!! THUD!
CRUD
NASTY MAG
THE THUDS
ORANGE
LIME GREEN
THUD!
POOR LOVE, I HOPE HE'S OK!! IT'S NOT EASY BEING TWENTY!

MR & MRS KING HAVE FOUND A SURGEON IN HARLEY STREET WHO CLAIMS TO BE..
WHO NEEDS IT!
WADAEVADUNFURME?
IT'S NOT GOING TO BE EASY BUT IT CAN BE DONE
*!!!
THIS FROM A NICE MIDDLE CLASS KID!
IT'S A BIT LATE FOR AN ABORTION
I'LL DO ANYTHING FOR MONEY
GOLD CARD
DINERS
..ABLE TO REMOVE BASEBALL HATS FROM THE HEADS OF TEENS. COULD THIS BE TRUE?

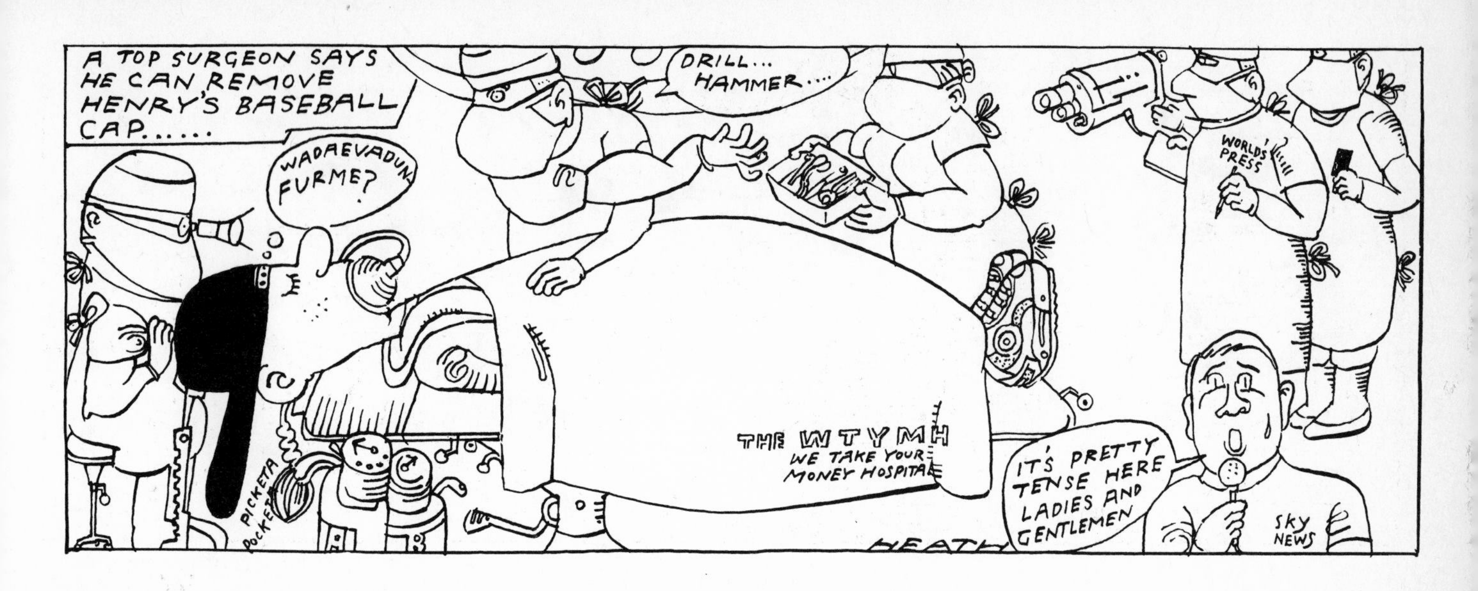
A TOP SURGEON SAYS HE CAN REMOVE HENRY'S BASEBALL CAP......
WADAEVADUN FURME?
DRILL... HAMMER....
WORLDS PRESS
THE WTYMH WE TAKE YOUR MONEY HOSPITAL
PICKETA POCKETA
IT'S PRETTY TENSE HERE LADIES AND GENTLEMEN
SKY NEWS
HEATH

HENRY IS RECUPERATING AFTER THE FAILED ATTEMPT TO REMOVE HIS BASEBALL CAP
WADYAEVADUNFURME?
OBSERVE THE PATIENT BEHIND ME. SEE HOW HE REACTS TO THE DEMANDS I PUT UPON HIM
HEATH
1
HAVE YOU EVER USED A KNIFE AND FORK?
BURP!
*!
!!
2
AT WHAT TIME DID YOU ARRIVE HOME LAST NIGHT?
*! YOU!
!*OFF
YOUR PARENTS WORRY ABOUT YOU. HOW DO YOU FEEL ABOUT THAT?
WADYAEVADUNFURME
*!
NEXT WEEK, WE WILL SEE HOW HE GETS ON AT SCHOOL

POLITICAL CARTOONS

(The *Spectator* and The *Independent*)

SINN FEIN TALKS EXCLUSIVE

FILM OF AN ALIEN THAT VISITED EARTH WILL BE SHOWN ON TELEVISION

HEATH
THEY'RE COMING
THE MILD BUNCH
NO ONE CAN STOP THEM!
CERT PC

2
The SUN
TONY BLAIR ATE OUR POLICIES
SAYS JOHN MAJOR
3 PHEW!
I'M ANYBODY'S!
MURDOCH BACKS BLAIR
MAYBE
TONY LIKES CUTTING TAXES. CHATTERING. CLEANING HIS TEETH. SMILING. SUITS. EUROPE. POWER....
HEATH

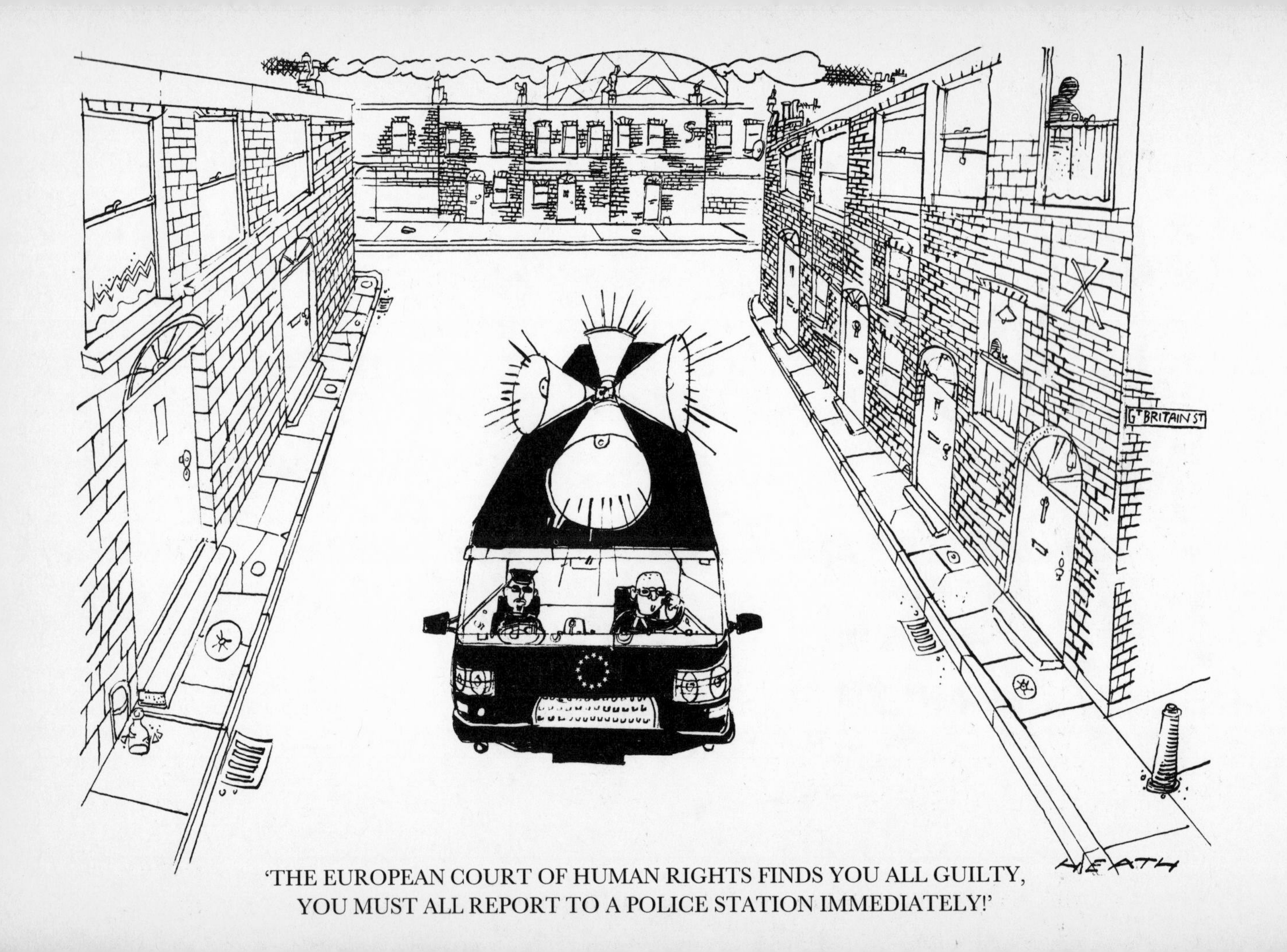

'THE EUROPEAN COURT OF HUMAN RIGHTS FINDS YOU ALL GUILTY, YOU MUST ALL REPORT TO A POLICE STATION IMMEDIATELY!'

WOMEN ARE NOW TAKING FAR MORE PLEASURE IN VIOLENCE (THINK TANK REPORT)

'WHAT ARE THE IMPLICATIONS OF CLONING SHEEP, DOCTOR?'

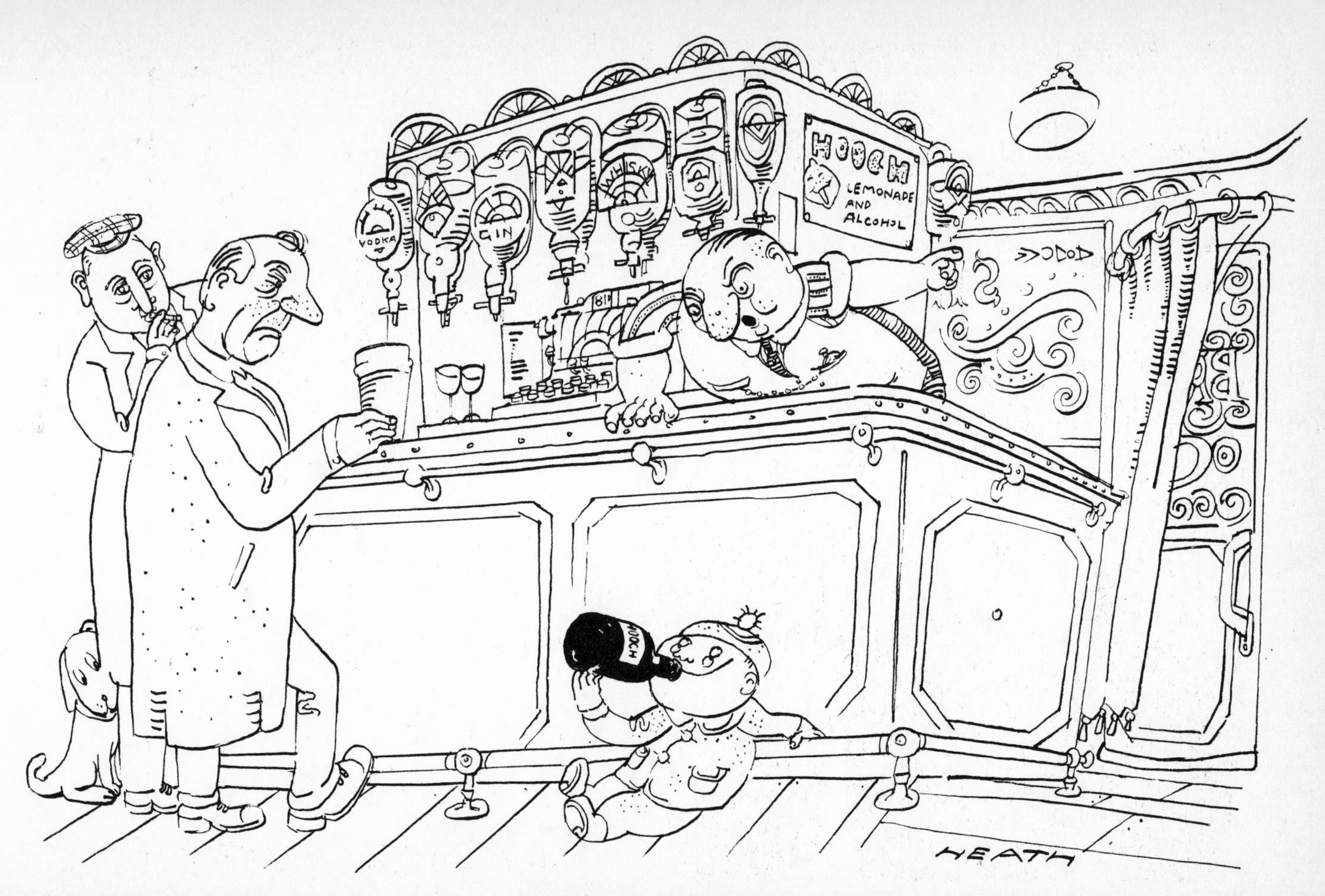

'YOU'VE HAD ENOUGH!'

PHOTO OPPORTUNITY

HEATH + du Maurier

THE QUEEN'S SPEECH
OK, ONE'S READY....
FROM THE TOP.....

MY GOVERNMENT....BLAH..BLAH..
....BLAH.....PROMISES...BLAH....
BLAH....

... HELLO? ONE WISHES TO
SPEAK WITH ONE'S AGENT...
LOOK LUV, DO I HAVE TO GO
THROUGH WITH THIS?....

VERY WELL, AS LONG AS
NOBODY THINKS THESE
ARE MY IDEAS....

THANK GOODNESS
THAT'S OVER!

HEATH
WHEEE!

THE REHEARSAL

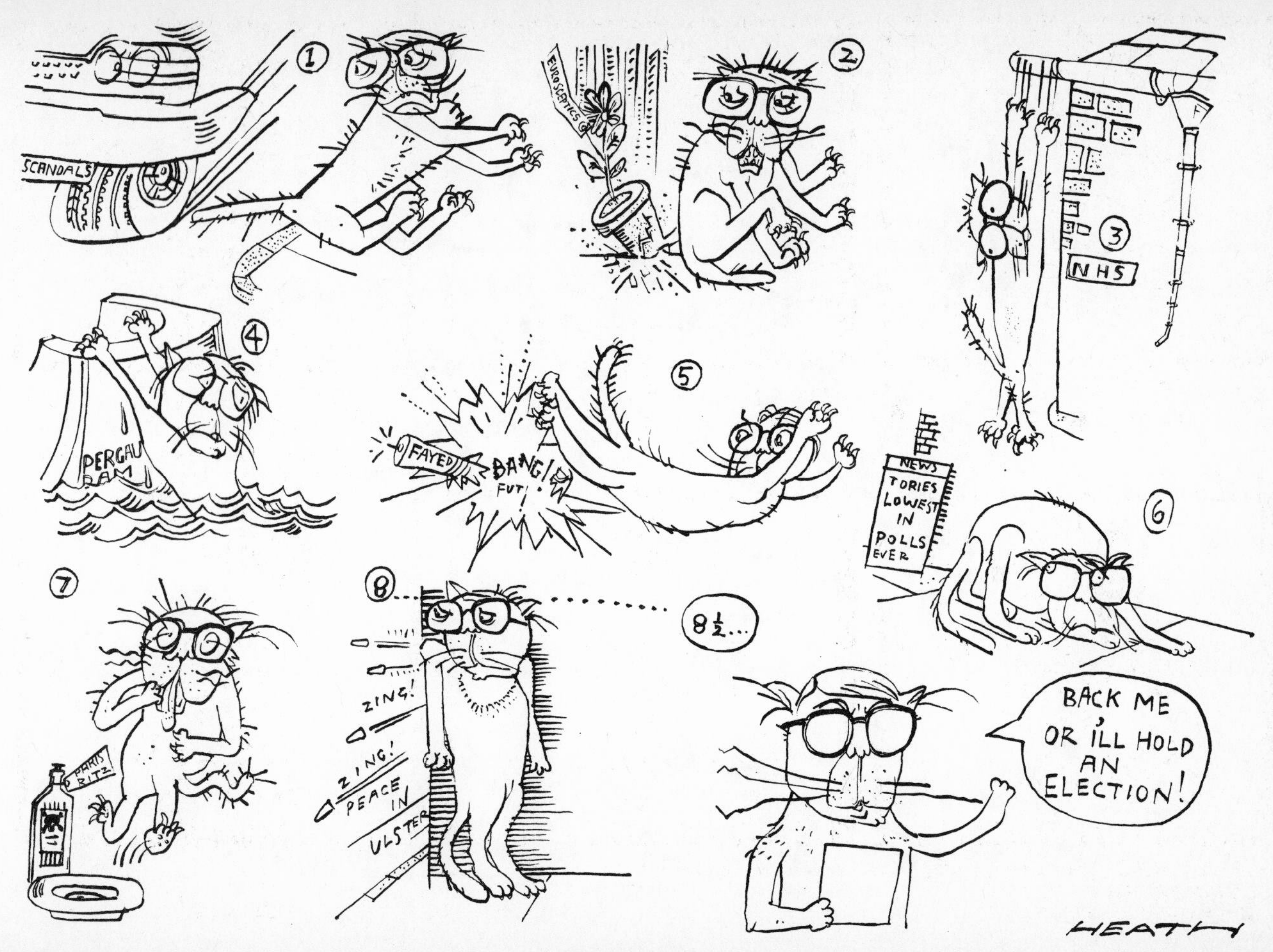
1
SCANDALS
2
EUROSCEPTICS
3
NHS
4
PERGAU DAM
5
FAYED
BANG!
FUT!
NEWS
TORIES LOWEST IN POLLS EVER
6
7
PARIS RITZ
8
ZING!
ZING!
PEACE IN ULSTER
8½...
BACK ME, OR I'LL HOLD AN ELECTION!
HEATH

NINE LIVES

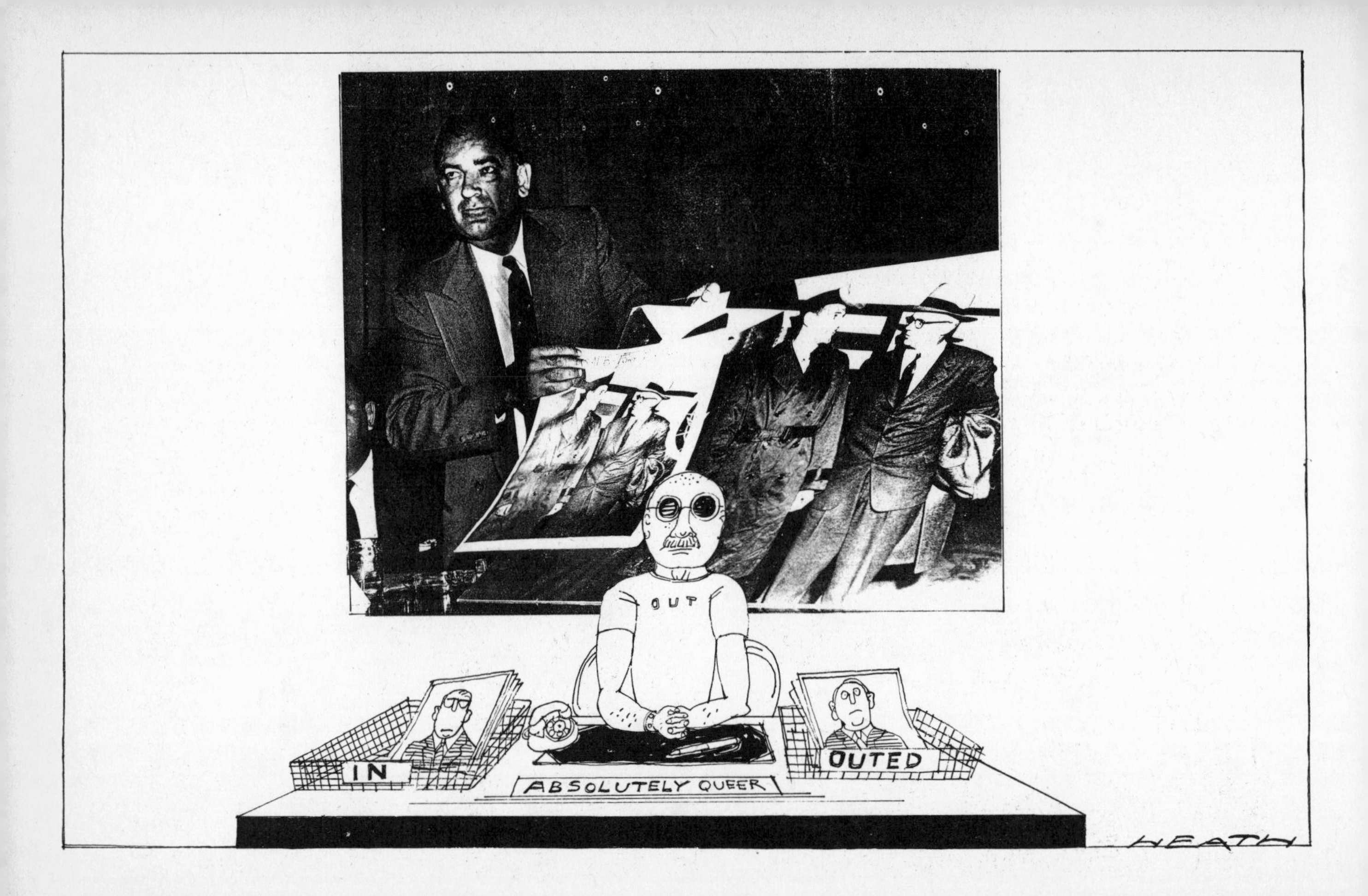
OUT
IN
OUTED
ABSOLUTELY QUEER
HEATH

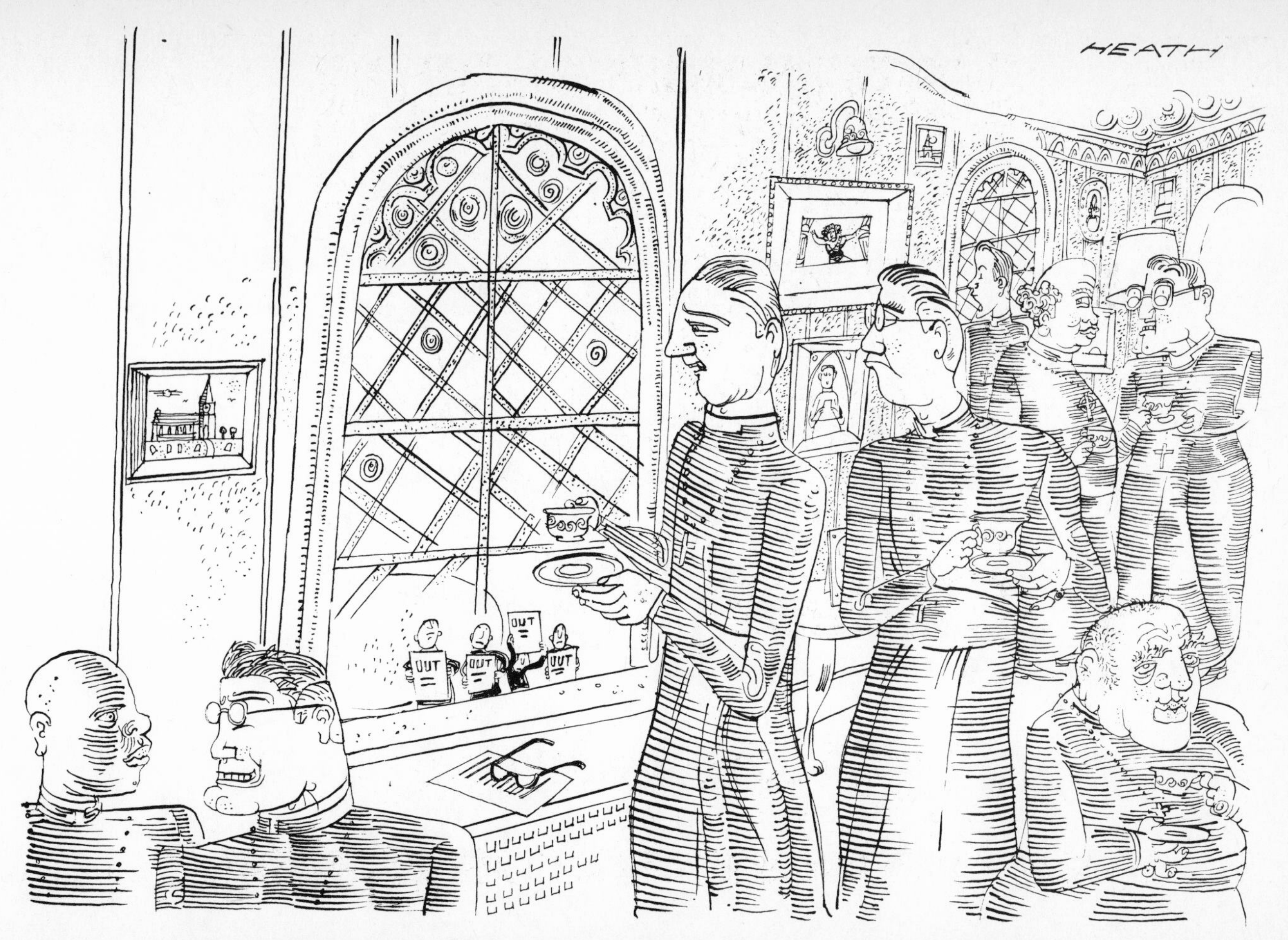

'I'VE LIVED WITH YOU FOR FIVE YEARS, JOHN, I NEVER KNEW YOU WERE GAY!'

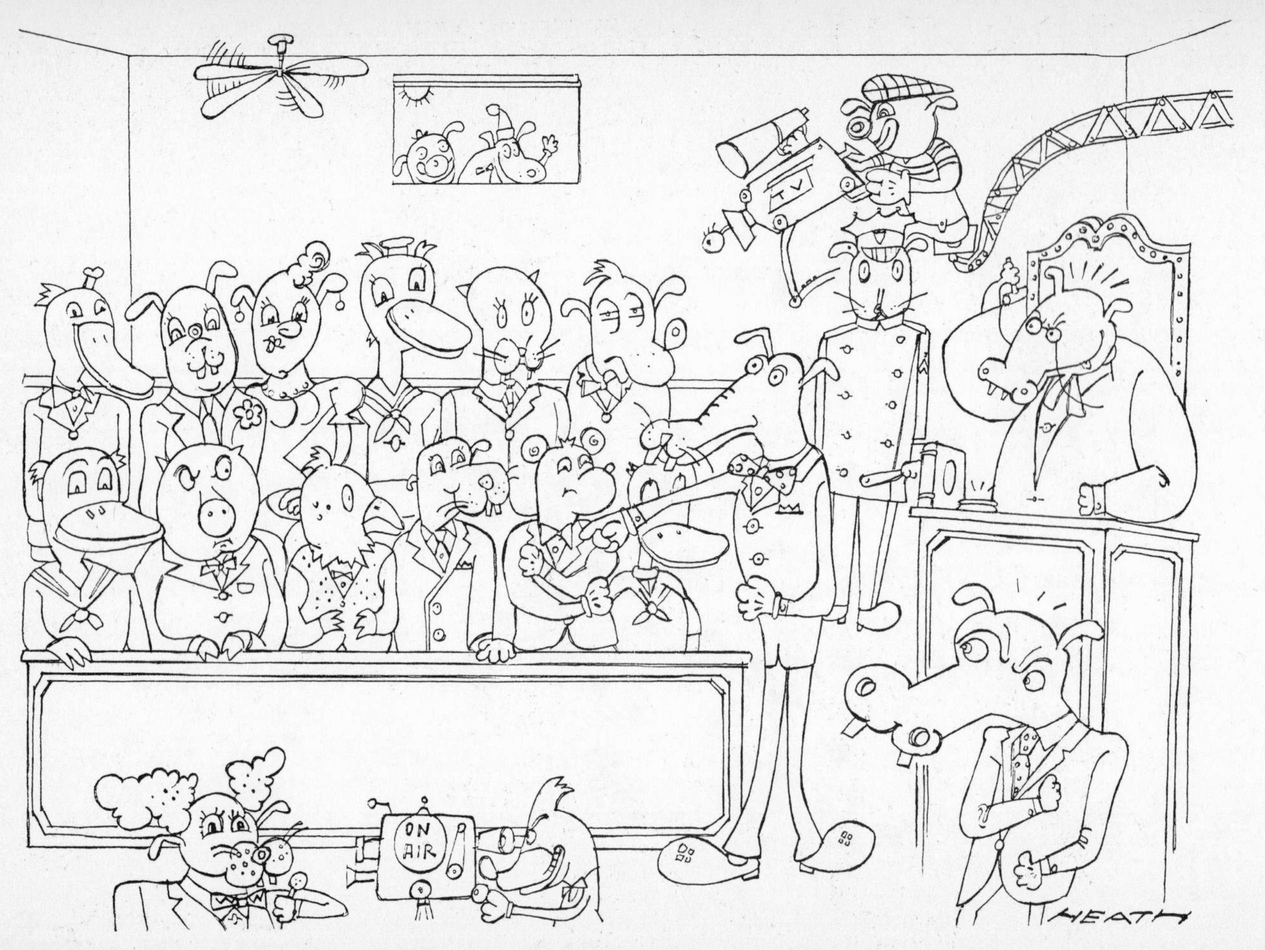

WEEK TWO OF THE O.J. SIMPSON TRIAL

THE ARK
OVERCROWDING IS CRUEL TO ANIMALS
UNFAIR TO ANIMALS
NOAH IS EVIL
ANIMAL RIGHTS NOW
FREE ALL ANIMALS
HEATH

'NURSES NEVER UNDERSTAND THAT THEIR VOCATION IS TO WORK, OUR VOCATION IS TO MAKE MONEY.'

'DON'T YOU REALISE HOW SILLY YOU LOOK, IN THAT OUTDATED PARAPHERNALIA?'

'WHICH ONE OF YOU IS MY FATHER?'

‘YER WE NEED DEALERS, HOW MANY ‘A’ LEVELS YOU GOT?’

NEWS
MENTALLY ILL LET BACK INTO COMMUN-ITY
HEATH

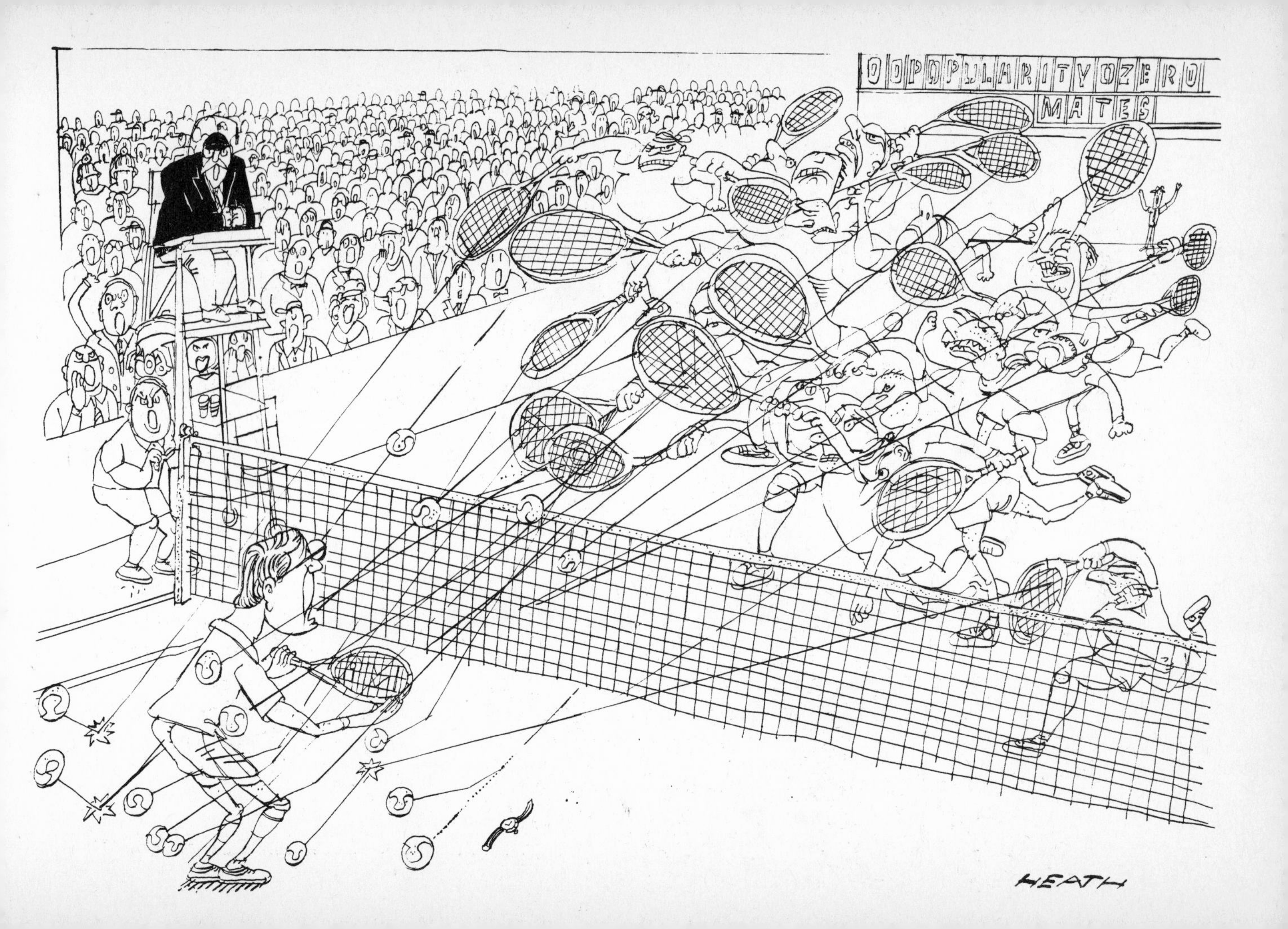
0 0 POPULARITY 0 ZERO
MATES
HEATH

POST OFFICE
YOU MAY TELEPHONE
YOU OLD COW!
1. THE VILLAGE GREEN
SCENES OF RURAL ENGLAND
YOU STINKIN' FILTH!
2. THE CHURCH
POLICE
CLOSED
3. VILLAGE BOBBY
4. GETAWAY
HEATH

'I SHOULDN'T BE HERE! I'M INNOCENT! IT WAS THE OTHER CHAP WHAT DID IT!'

STAGE
DOOR
GOOD LUCK
GERRY DARLING! YOU WERE WONDERFUL!
IRA
HEATH

SHOW BIZ

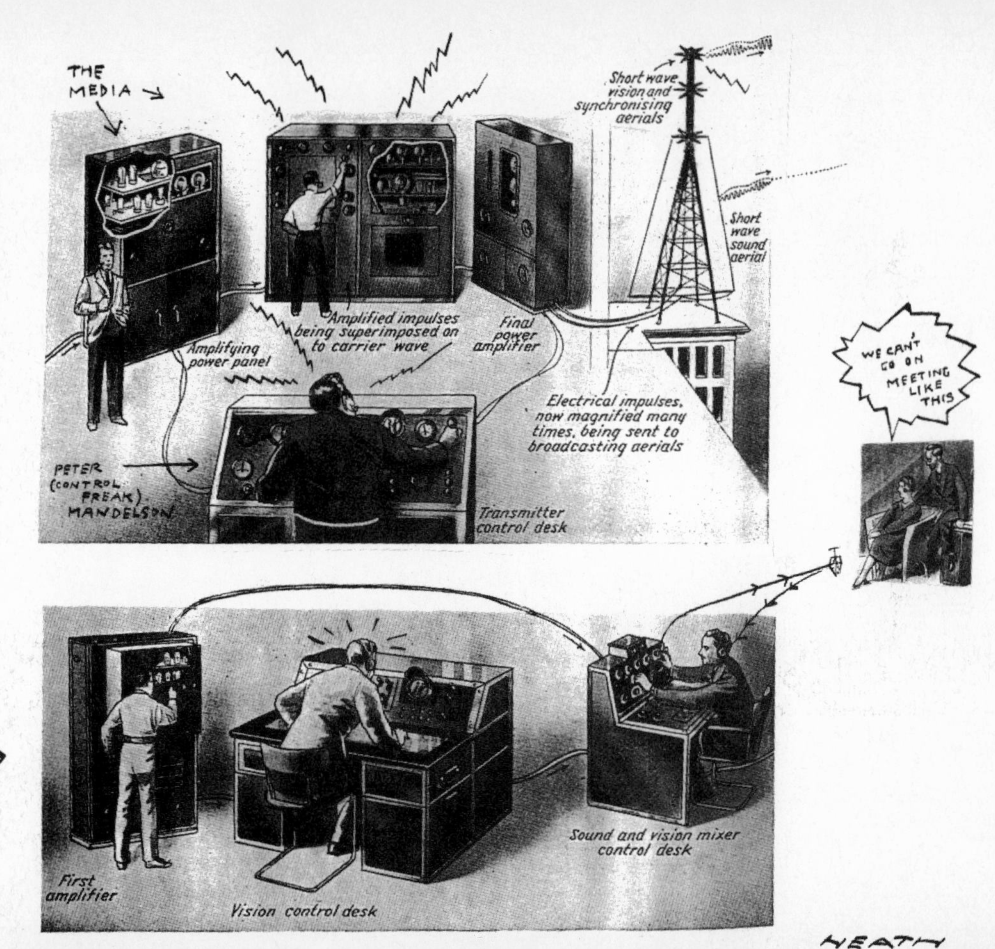
WONDERS OF THE WORLD No 97
THE MEDIA
Short wave vision and synchronising aerials
Short wave sound aerial
Amplified impulses being superimposed on to carrier wave
Final power amplifier
Amplifying power panel
Electrical impulses, now magnified many times, being sent to broadcasting aerials
PETER (CONTROL FREAK) MANDELSON
Transmitter control desk
WE CAN'T GO ON MEETING LIKE THIS
The Cab-e-net.
HOW PETER (CONTROL FREAK) MANDELSON CONTROLS THE NEW LABOUR MINISTERS
First amplifier
Vision control desk
Sound and vision mixer control desk
HEATH

INDULGE IN
RUBBER!
CHAINS!
FLEX!
ORANGES!
CONSERVATIVE
CENTRAL
OFFICE
SLEAZY
CLUB
SEX! SEX! SEX!
KINKY
GEAR
TV
AS SEEN
TV!
SEX! SEX!
PEEP
SHOW→
BACK TO BASICS
TALK DIRTY!
LET YOUR
SELF BE
DOMINATED
HEATH

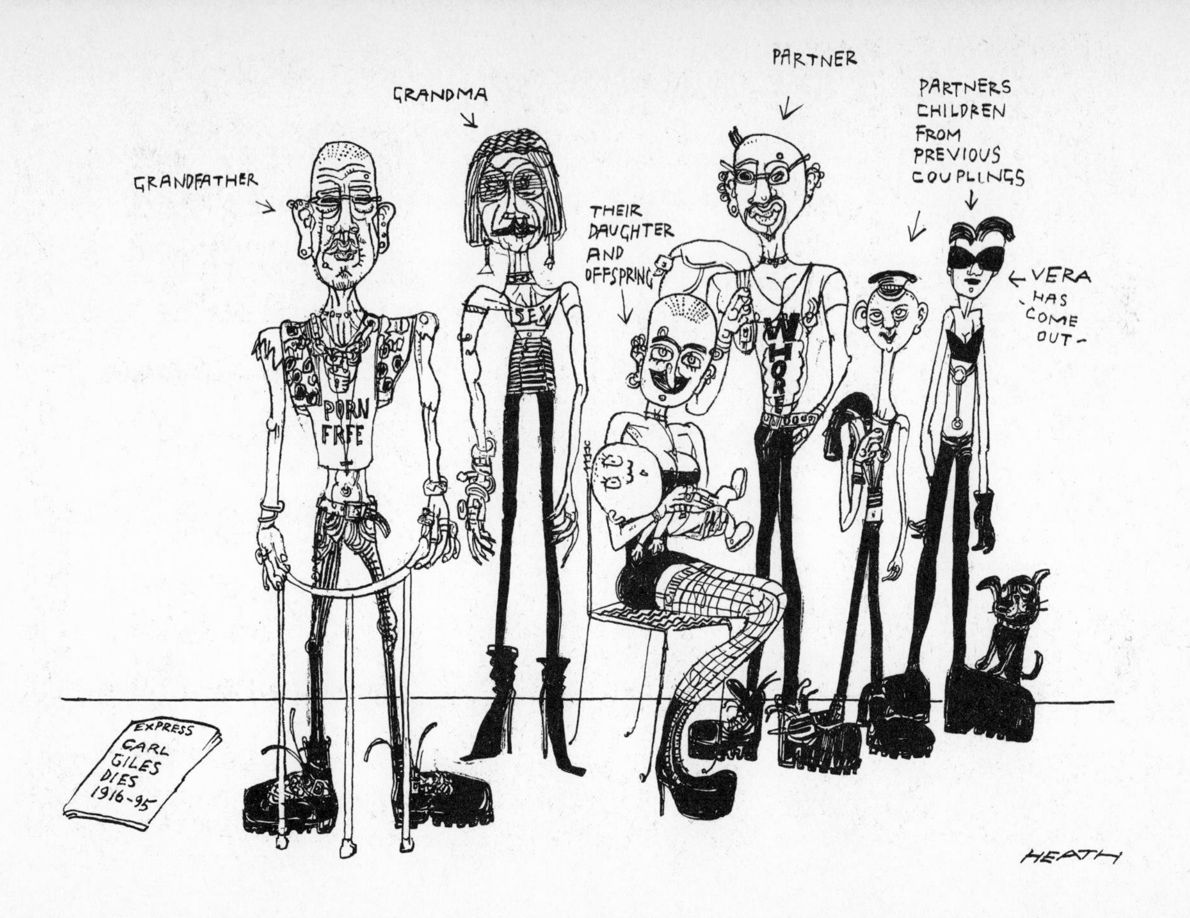

WHAT THE TYPICAL FAMILY LOOKS LIKE TODAY, IF GILES WERE ALIVE TO DRAW THEM

'IT'LL COST YOU!'

'YOU'RE NOT MAD, BUT YOU ARE A LITTLE DEPRESSED.'

THE HORRORS OF WAR. HAITI 1994

HELLO IS THAT 'HELLO'?
BY APPOINTMENT
ALL THE NICE GIRLS LOVE A SAILOR
"KRUG CHAMP
THIS TIME IT'S FOR KEEPS
ID BETTER DO ANOTHER HEAD COUNT
INLAND REV FINAL DEMAND
HUMPH!
WATCH THE BIRDY
SPORTING LIFE
10/1 EVENS SEPARATION 6/2

35
BILL HAGUE AND THE COMETS
WE CAN'T GET NO SATISFACTION
HEATH

RETURNS
OH, RIGHT. YOU STILL GOT YOUR RECEIPT?
WAH!
WE WANT ANOTER ONE, THIS ONE CRIES ALL THE TIME!
YER, YOU CAN'T HEAR THE TELLY, KNOW WHAT I MEAN?
BEST BEFORE 1995
Kid·U·Like TM
SALE
NOW ON
INSTANT KIDDY
ALL MAJOR CREDIT CARDS
I'M NOT SURE, CAN WE THINK ABOUT IT?
I'M NOT HAPPY ABOUT THE COLOUR, WILL THEY MATCH THE CURTAINS?
THESE ARE SELLING WELL AT THE MOMENT
BOY WHITE WEIGHT 8lb 5oz
GIRL WHITE WEIGHT 6lb 8oz
HEATH

CHANNEL TUNNEL
WE APOLOGISE FOR THE LATE ARRIVAL OF THIS TUNNEL ......
35

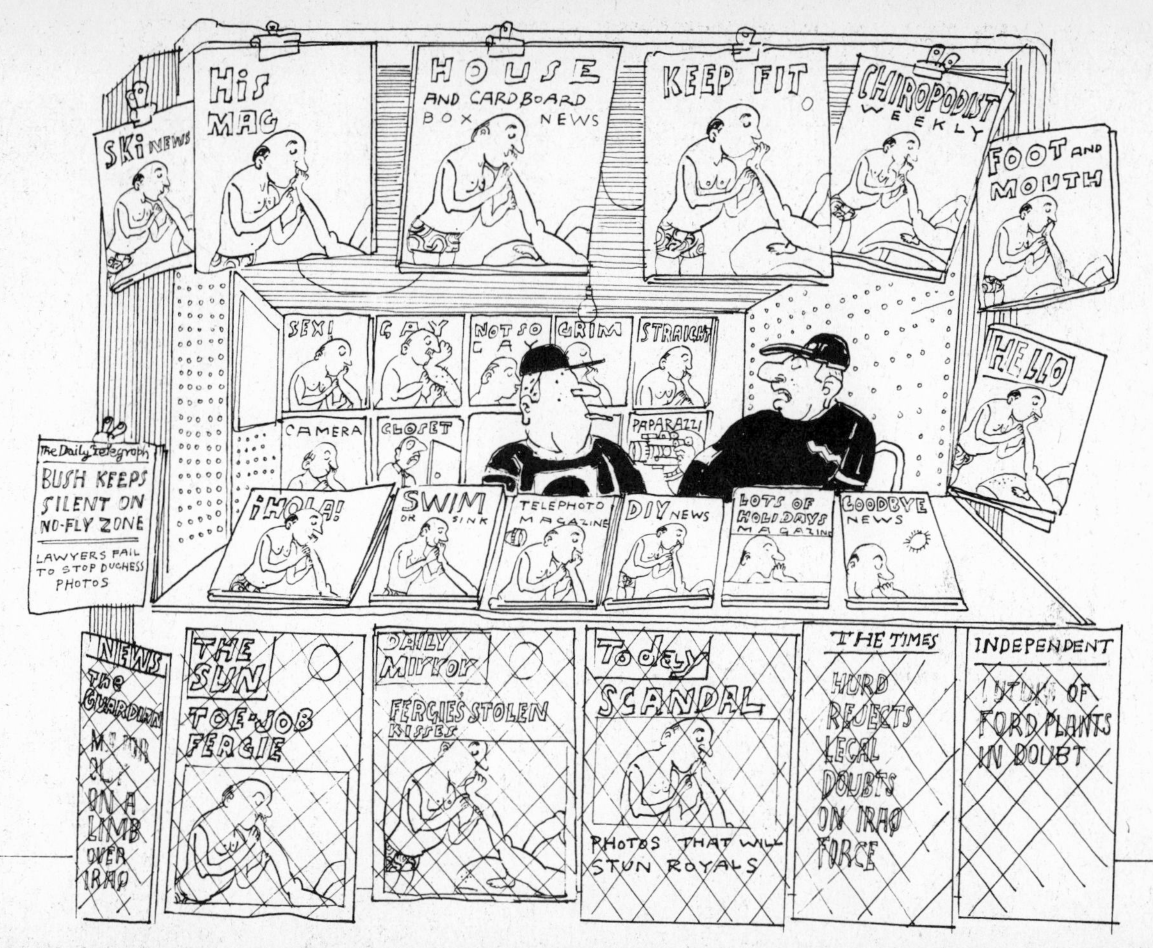

'PERSONALLY I FIND IT ALL LEAVES A RATHER NASTY TASTE IN ONE'S MOUTH.'

'I SAY CHAPS! IT'S SNEAKY BUNTER TAKING PICTURES OF PRINCE WILLIAM FOR SOME ROTTEN TABLOID!'

'I'M GONNA PUT 'IM DOWN, HE DOESN'T ATTACK ANYBODY!'

EXIT
CHECK OUT
DEEP FREEZE
FREE SPERM OFFER!
BOYS
GAY
STRAIGHT
BOYS
COLOUR
HEIGHT
GIRLS
COLOUR
GAY
LESBIAN
BOYS
A+WHITE
UPPER MIDDLE CLASS
GIRLS
AFRO-CARIBBEAN
HEIGHT
EYE COLOUR
GIRLS
ASIAN CHINESE
DREK
FUT
SUD
GRUT
HEATH

The feeling is of intense isolation... despair even....
A metaphor for loss and yet....
AWAY FROM THE FLOCK. by DAMIEN HIRST
HEATH
WITH APOLOGIES

BRINGING UP FATHER

TONY BLAIR CLOTHES FOR NEW LABOUR MEN
AUTUMN COLLECTION

CLOTH CAPS £850. NECK CHOKER. £750. CASHMERE ROLL-NECK £900. COLLARLESS SHIRT £105
WOOLLEN SUIT £1.900. STOUT WALKING BOOTS. £799. PARFUMS ARMANI. MEDALS £2000+VAT
PHOTO SHOOT: BRIGHTON

LOOK AT HIS EYES!
LOOK AT THE WAY HE WALKS!
MILL-BANK
TIME FOR A CHANGE
HEATH

'THERE MUST BE SOME MISTAKE OFFICER, YOU'VE GOT THE RIGHT MAN!'

MAIL ON SUNDAY

'I DOUBT IF EVEN PETER MANDELSON COULD CONTROL HIM!'

'I THINK I'LL VOTE TORY, AT LEAST THEY ARE SEXY!'

'I'M SENTENCING YOU TO FIVE YEARS NEW LABOUR!'

'GET YOUR OWN BACK MR WILL SELF, DON'T VOTE CONSERVATIVE!'

'YOU MAY WEAR THE GRIN, BUT I WEAR THE TROUSERS!'

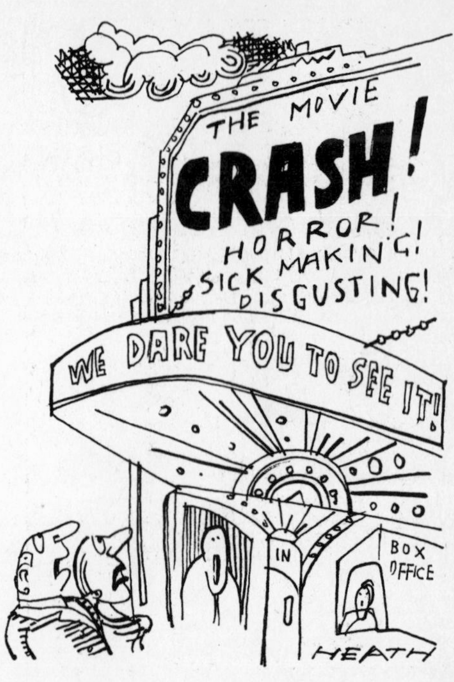

'OH, LORD! THEY'VE MADE A FILM ABOUT THE TORY PARTY ALREADY!'

'THE MAGAZINE WEIGHS MORE THAN ITS MODELS!'

'WHAT ABOUT THE BOSSES?'

'IT SEEMS TO ME, THAT KIDS TODAY NEED SOMEONE THEY CAN LOOK DOWN ON!'

THE BLAIRS

(The *Spectator*)

OK, AT LAST I'VE THOUGHT OF A NEW STRIP →
CHERIE, DARLING, I CAN'T FIND MY NEW GEORGIO ARMANI!
!
TOOTHLESS AND DE-BARKED
PRESCOTT
I HOPE, YOU DONT MIND, DARLING I GAVE THEM TO THE POOR HOMELESS PEOPLE
OH, MY DARLING, SOUND-BITE! OF COURSE I DON'T MIND. I WISH I'D THOUGHT OF IT
GET DOWN PRESCOTT, GOOD BOY!
!
HEATH ©

POPPET! DID YOU REMEMBER TO GET THE SPECIAL FOOD FOR OUR GUESTS TONIGHT?
YES, AND IT WASN'T EASY!
WELL, YOU SEE I DON'T WANT TO GIVE THE IMPRESSION THAT WE'VE CUT....
OURSELVES OFF FROM OUR ROOTS
SSHHH!
YES, BUT YOU CAN ONLY GET PEAS PUDDING, TRIPE AN' ONIONS AN' SPOTTED DICK AT HARRODS FOOD HALL...
...AND IT COSTS A BLOODY FORTUNE!
PRESCOTT
HEATH

'ERE WHAT YOU ASKIN' MY BOY?
I'M GLAD YOU ASKED ME THAT, NO, LET ME FINISH, IF YOU WILL JUST LET ME ANSWER THE QUESTION! WE, IN THE NEW LABOUR PARTY, MY LABOUR PARTY! WANT EVERY ONE TO KNOW THE TIME REGARDLESS OF RACE, CREED, OR COLOUR, I KNOW IT WAS SAID THAT I TOLD THE TIME BACK IN 1991, BUT NOW, LET ME FINISH, YOU'VE HAD YOUR SAY, BUT THINGS HAVE CHANGED SINCE 1991, THE TIME IS NOT THE SAME TIME, IT'S TIME FOR A CHANGE..............
PLEASE, COULD YOU TELL ME THE TIME?
I'LL BUY MYSELF A NICE ROLEX!
HEATH

NO HIGHER TAXES! A BETTER EDUCATION FOR ALL! MORE JOBS!
ALL PAID FOR BY A WINDFALL TAX..... NURSERY SCHOOLING...
SOMEWHERE OVER THE RAINBOW BLUEBIRDS FLY OVER THE RAINBOW, WHY THEN, OH WHY CAN'T I? THERE'S A PLACE THAT I DREAMED OF ONCE IN A LULLABY.....
HEATH

NEW LABOUR IS ON ITS WAY...
BACK OFF!
COME IN, MILLBANK!
HI! CALL ME TONY
MOVE ON! OUT OF THE WAY FOR OUR LEADER TO BE!
SOUND BITE 1 TO SOUNDBITE 2!
TIME FOR A CHANGE
COME ON NOW WE DON'T WANT ANY TROUBLE
BUT WE ARE SOCIALISTS!
WE HAVE LIFT OFF! GO FOR IT!
I'M NOT GIVING UP MY DAYJOB!
HEATH

BLAIR BABY WE LUV YER!
CHERIE PULL OUT!
AT LAST, A LEADER WE CAN BE PROUD OF... YOUNG, HANDSOME, INCORRUPTIBLE, SELFLESS, ALL THINGS TO ALL MEN, A SMILE TO KILL, A SENSE OF HUMOUR!! CLEAN LIVING, CHARMING... DARE I SAY IT, VERY, VERY, SEXY! HERE'S LOOKING AT YOU, KID! TIME FOR A CHANGE! WOW! I DON'T KNOW WHAT IT IS, BUT YOU'VE GOT IT! IF IT AIN'T BROKE DON'T FIX IT!....
THE SUN
WHO LUVS YER BABY?
SHAVE
HEATH

NEW LABOUR'S TRIBUTE TO ALFRED HITCHCOCK'S 'REBECCA'

WITH THANKS TO THE EDITORS OF:

The *Independent*
The *Spectator*
Private Eye
Mail on Sunday